A.G. Sirota

POLYOLEFINS

MODIFICATION OF
STRUCTURE AND PROPERTIES

Translated from Russian
by J. Schmorak

Israel Program for Scientific Translations
Jerusalem 1971

This book is a translation of

MODIFIKATSIYA STRUKTURY
I SVOISTV POLIOLEFINOV
Izdatel'stvo "Khimiya"
Leningrad 1969

IPST Cat. No. 2229

Printed and Bound in Israel
Printed in Jerusalem by Keter Press
Binding: Wiener Bindery Ltd., Jerusalem

Table of Contents

17329

INTRODUCTION

Polyolefins have become one of the most important kinds of synthetic polymeric materials during the past few years. The global production of polyethylene alone was 2,320,000 tons in 1964 (Chap. I /1, 2/), while the increase in the production volume between 1950 and 1963 was on the average 38.3% per year (Chap. I /3/). The extent and scope of utilization of polypropylene, poly-α-butylene, poly-3-methylbutene-1, poly-4-methylpentene-1 and other polymers keep increasing. Nevertheless, the number of industrially manufactured polyolefins is limited, while the number of articles made from these polymers becomes larger. This is due to the different ways in which these polymers can be modified; as a result, their scope of application can be extended and it becomes possible, to some extent at least, to monitor their physical parameters as desired.

Polyolefins have a number of very valuable properties: high dielectric parameters which are preserved over a wide range of temperatures, chemical stability, considerable resistance to heat and often also satisfactory resistance to cold, high mechanical strength, low density, etc. Very often, however, it is these very properties which prevent the material from being used for a specific purpose. Thus, for instance, the low polarity of polyolefins renders them highly dielectric and chemically inert, but at the same time is responsible for their limited adhesion to certain materials and for their poor takeup of dyes. Highly crystalline and totally crystalline linear species of polyethylene have a high mechanical strength and resistance to heat, but at the same time are inelastic and are liable to crack under prolonged stress and also due to other causes.

The modification of polyolefins, which is generally accompanied by some structural changes, may also be effected in order to change some of the properties of the material as desired, while leaving its other properties unchanged.

The deliberate alteration of the structure and properties of polyolefins may be effected during the synthesis, or by means of operations carried out on the finished polymer product. An example of the former procedure is the variation of the polymerization parameters and copolymerization of α-olefins with different monomers. Modification of the ready-made poly-α-olefins is achieved by introducing functional groups into the polymer molecule, by forming a system of covalent or ionic bonds between the macromolecular chains, by making formulations with various polymeric and low-molecular substances and also by treatments which combine the different modification techniques.

The modification techniques of polyolefins are largely connected with their individual properties. Thus, if the polymer is chemically inert, reactions which can be conducted in the polymer chain are few, and the

1

low chemical reactivity must then be overcome by special techniques. On the other hand, if the degree of crystallinity of polyethylene is varied by varying the conditions of crystallization or by altering its molecular structure, it is possible to alter the supermolecular structure, and thus also many of the properties of the material.

Differences in the structure of polyolefins also determine the modification techniques which are suitable for the particular polymer. Thus, for example, since each repeating unit in polypropylene contains a tertiary carbon atom, oxidation products can be obtained under milder conditions than in the case of polyethylene, and can then be used directly or can be employed in further transformations. Again, if polypropylene is modified by radiation, it must be borne in mind that the tertiary carbon atoms are unstable to ionizing radiation and the material is degraded as a result. The degradation of polyethylene under these conditions is much less extensive; polyethylene can, accordingly, be irradiated in order to improve its resistance to heat and also for other purposes.

Chapter I

STRUCTURE AND PROPERTIES OF POLYOLEFINS

POLYETHYLENE

The structure and properties of polyethylene form the subject of abundant literature /4 — 10/. We shall limit ourselves, accordingly, to a brief account of the structure and properties of polyethylene and the possibilities of modification of these properties by varying the conditions of the synthesis.

Many types of polyethylene are industrially produced; they are manufactured under high, medium and low pressures. If the conditions of polymerization of ethylene are changed, the structure and the properties of the final product will be different as well. However, even when the same polymerization technique is employed, different products may be obtained by varying the working parameters which determine the structure and properties of polyethylene.

Polymerization of ethylene under high pressures (1,000 — 3,000 atm) obeys the relationships governing ordinary free radical polymerization of vinyl compounds. If the polymerization of ethylene has been initiated by free radicals, a high molecular weight product will only be obtained if the monomer concentration is high. If this concentration is low, the monomer still adds onto the free radicals, but the deactivation of free radicals competes with the reaction of chain propagation, and the resulting polymer has a low molecular weight /11 — 13/. If the pressure of ethylene is increased, its density increases as a result, and the average molecular weight of the polymer obtained at a given temperature and initiator concentration increases.

The density of ethylene can also be increased by reducing the temperature. The lower temperature limit will depend on the identity of the initiator of the polymerization. The polymerization is usually performed between 80 and 300°C.

The molecular weight of polyethylene is inversely proportional to the temperature and initiator concentration and is usually between 2,000 and 40,000.

The degree of branching of the macromolecules, which largely determines the nature of crystalline formations and thus also the properties of the final product, is also a function of the temperature. The higher the polymerization temperature, the higher the degree of branching. Branch formation is mainly caused by chain transfer reactions /14/, the rate of which increases with the temperature. The branches formed as a result may have differing lengths. The relationship between the branch length distribution and the conditions of polymerization has not been studied, but it is assumed that at higher temperatures the branches become longer /11/.

As the number of side chains — as determined by IR spectroscopy — increases, the degree of crystallinity decreases and those physical and mechanical properties of the polymer which depend on the degree of crystallinity deteriorate: density, resistance to heat, mechanical strength, stiffness, etc.

The properties of both solid and molten polyethylene undoubtedly depend on the length of the side chains as well, but the study of this relationship is difficult, since a method for the determination of the length of the side chains, especially if they are relatively long, is not yet available. As regards short side chains, it is believed that these are mainly constituted by butyl and ethyl groups /15/. Studies made on model copolymers of ethylene with higher α-olefins showed that ethyl and butyl side chains interfere most strongly with the crystallization of the polymer /16, 17/.

Polymerization by ionizing radiation, in which the free radicals are regenerated by γ-rays /18 — 23/ is readily monitored so as to impart the desired properties to the final product. Depending on the experimental conditions, the polymers may be liquid, of waxlike consistency, or solid. The molecular weight of the product is higher, the higher the pressure and the lower the temperature of polymerization. Below 80°C solid polyethylene is obtained, in which the degree of branching is low. At higher temperatures waxlike and liquid products are obtained.

Polymerization of ethylene under low pressures (up to 5 atm) in the presence of organometallic complex catalysts is an anionic process, as a result of which the structure and properties of the final product are affected in an altogether different manner. The polymerization is effected in a hydrocarbon solvent at 60 — 80°C. The catalyst is present in the solvent as a precipitate or a colloidal dispersion. The catalysts are prepared by reacting alkyls of metals of Groups I, II and III (most often alkylaluminum compounds) with salts of metals of variable valency (usually chlorides of titanium or vanadium). It is assumed /24 — 26/ that the metal-carbon bonds in the catalyst complex are strongly polarized, which results in the formation of a carbanion; the monomer molecules attack the bond between the metal and the carbanion and the growing anion is coordinated with the metal cation.

The principal method for the modification of the properties of polyethylene is to vary the identity of the catalyst complex. Thus, if an alkylaluminum halide (e. g., diethylaluminum chloride) is used instead of an alkylaluminum compound (e. g., triethylaluminum), the molecular weight of the polymer decreases /27/. The molecular weight and also the molecular weight distribution can be largely regulated by varying the ratio between the alkylaluminum compound and titanium chloride /28, 29/. Thus, if the molar ratio triethylaluminum : titanium tetrachloride is 2 : 1, the polyethylene has a molecular weight of 1,000,000, while if this ratio is 1 : 2, the product is brittle and has a molecular weight below 30,000. If the aluminum : titanium ratio in the catalyst is close to unity, the molecular weight of the polyethylene product is 70,000 — 350,000, and it can be injection-molded or extruded at a relatively low temperature (200 — 260°C).

The molecular weight of the polyethylene product can also be reduced by the addition of hydrogen, which causes chain transfer and chain termination. If it is desired to obtain a polymer with a narrow distribution of molecular weights, the polymerization should be effected in the presence of a small amount of carbon monoxide /30/ or the ethylene diluted with an inert gas prior to polymerization /31/.

Since the polymerization on organometallic catalysts proceeds by an ionic mechanism, the degree of branching of the macromolecules is very low. The linear chain structure is responsible for the high degree of ordering (crystallization) of low-pressure polyethylene; as a result, the technical parameters (density, mechanical strength, stiffness, heat resistance) of the product are superior to those displayed by high-pressure polyethylene.

Even less branched and more highly crystalline products are obtained by ionic polymerization of ethylene on solid metal oxide catalysts under medium pressure (35 − 70 atm). The process is realized in a hydrocarbon solvent medium at 100 − 275°C. It is catalyzed by oxides of chromium /32 − 34/, molybdenum, nickel and cobalt /35 − 42/.

Chromium oxides are most often deposited onto a porous aluminum silicate support. In the case of molybdenum oxide the supports are aluminum oxide and titanium oxide, while activated carbon is employed as support for nickel and cobalt oxides. The catalysts are activated prior to use; thus, for instance, chromium oxide is heated at 500 − 600°C in a stream of dry air for several hours.

The temperature of the process largely determines the molecular weight and the related properties of the polyethylene product. If the polymerization temperature is increased, the molecular weight of the product shows a considerable drop and the melt index increases correspondingly /41/. Thus, when the temperature was raised from 100 to 135°C, polyethylene which had been polymerized on a chromium oxide catalyst had an intrinsic viscosity of 2.4 to 0.8 dl/g/34, 43, 44/.

The molecular weight also depends on the activation temperature of the catalyst: the higher the activation temperature, the lower the molecular weight of the polymer /34, 41/.

If the polymerization pressure is increased, the rate of the reaction is much accelerated. The molecular weight of the product also increases but not to the extent attained by decreasing the polymerization temperature /34, 43 − 45/.

The mechanism of polymerization of ethylene determines yet another structural parameter of the polymer − the identity of the unsaturated groups. Table 1 shows the contents of unsaturated groups in various types of polyethylene; these data were reported by Goldenberg et al. /34, 46/ and are in good agreement with the data of Smith /47/.

It is seen from the table that the unsaturated groups in high-pressure polyethylene are mostly vinylidene groups. They are formed by chain transfer reactions involving polymer molecules originating from the free radical polymerization of ethylene /46/. The chain transfer reactions, which are rapid at elevated temperatures, result in the formation of active sites on the carbon atoms of polyethylene macromolecules:

$$\cdots -CH_2-CH_2-\underset{\underset{R}{|}}{C}-CH_2-\cdots$$

5

TABLE 1. Various unsaturated groups in polyethylene /34/

Polyethylene	Number of $\diagdown C=C \diagup$ groups per 1,000 C-atoms	Group content, %		
		vinyl $\underset{R}{\overset{H}{\diagdown}} C=CH_2$	vinylidene $\underset{R'}{\overset{R}{\diagdown}} C=CH_2$	trans-vinylene $\underset{R}{\overset{H}{\diagdown}} C=C \underset{H}{\overset{R'}{\diagup}}$
High pressure	0.3—0.4	17	71	12
Low pressure	0.3—0.4	52	31	17
Medium pressure	1.1—1.3	87	7	6

It is assumed that vinylidene groups are formed by the reaction:

$$\cdots -CH_2-CH_2-\overset{\bullet}{\underset{R}{C}}-CH_2-\cdots \longrightarrow \cdots -\overset{\bullet}{C}H_2+CH_2=\underset{R}{C}-CH_2-\cdots$$

The mechanism of formation of double bonds in polyethylene prepared on ionic catalysts is less clear. It is believed, however /46/, that double bonds in low-pressure polyethylene are formed by disproportionation resulting from the transfer of the hydride ion from the β-carbon atom to the metal /48, 49/:

$$M^+ \cdots {}^-CH_2-CH_2-CH_2-\cdots \longrightarrow MH+CH_2=CH-CH_2-\cdots$$

This mechanism of termination of the growing chain yields mainly vinyl groups; if there is a substituent at the β-carbon atom, vinylidene groups are formed. It is seen from Table 1 that the unsaturated groups in low-pressure polyethylene in fact consist mostly of vinyl groups.

Vinyl groups also account for most of the unsaturated groups in medium-pressure polyethylene. If it is assumed that the polymerization mechanism of ethylene on oxide catalysts is ionic /50/, the formation of vinyl groups can be represented by the reaction:

$$X(CH_2-CH_2)_n-CH_2-CH_2^+ \longrightarrow X(CH_2-CH_2)_n-CH=CH_2+H^+$$

in which chain termination is effected by the cleavage of a proton off the methylene group next to the active end of the molecular.

The individual features of the molecular structure which originate from the various mechanisms and conditions of polymerization, in particular the degree of branching, clearly determine the important properties of individual samples of polyethylene. Table 2 shows the most important data on the structure and properties of high-pressure, low-pressure and medium-pressure polyethylene.

The different properties of the different products are the result of the different degrees of branching of the macromolecules, since it is the degree of branching which is the paramount factor in determining the crystallinity of polyethylene. The most highly branched high-pressure polyethylene has a low crystallinity, low density, low melting point, low tensile strength, low stiffness and low hardness. The least branched medium-pressure

6

polyethylene, on the contrary, is almost totally crystalline, much denser, much more stiff, much harder and has a higher melting point. The low-pressure polyethylene has an intermediate degree of branching, and thus displays intermediate values of these parameters.

TABLE 2. Properties of different types of polyethylene

Parameter	High-pressure polyethylene	Low-pressure polyethylene	Medium-pressure polyethylene
Intrinsic viscosity in decalin at 135°C, dl/g . .	0.7—1.0	1.0—5.1	1.2—3.0
Number of CH_3 groups per 1,000 C-atoms . . .	20—40	5—15	1.5—5.0
Crystallinity, %	53—67	80—90	85—93
Density, g/cm³	0.92—0.93	0.94—0.96	0.96—0.97
Melting point, °C	108—110	120—134	127—130
Tensile strength, kg/cm²	120—160	220—350	270—330
Flexural strength, kg/cm²	120—170	200—380	250—400
Yield point, kg/cm².	100—110	200—250	250—300
Elongation at break, % (extension rate 100 mm/min)	150—600	200—900	20—400
Elasticity modulus, kg/cm²	1,500—2,500	5,500—8,000	8,000—10,500
Brinell hardness, kg/mm²	1.4—2.4	4.5—5.8	5.6—6.5
Water absorption after 30 days at 20°C, % . . .	0.04	0.03—0.04	0.01
Dielectric loss factor at $10^6 sec^{-1}$ and 20°C	$2 \cdot 10^{-4}$—$4 \cdot 10^{-4}$	$2 \cdot 10^{-4}$—$6 \cdot 10^{-4}$	$2 \cdot 10^{-4}$—$4 \cdot 10^{-4}$
Dielectric constant at $10^6 sec^{-1}$	2.2—2.3	2.1—2.4	2.3
Electric volume resistivity, ohm·cm	10^{17}	10^{17}	10^{17}
Dielectric strength, AC:			
1 mm thick sample, kV/mm	45—60	45—60	45—60
2 mm thick sample, kV/mm	28—35	28—36	29—31

As the degree of branching increases, the crystallinity decreases owing to the impairments in the crystal structure at the branching points and in their vicinity. Density, melting point, elasticity modulus and hardness are related to small displacements of molecules in the solid polyethylene, which means that their values vary strongly with the extent of crystallinity /51/. The properties of polyethylene related to major deformations (tensile strength, elongation at break and brittleness temperature) depend not only on the degree of branching and crystallinity, but even more so on the molecular weight of polyethylene /52/.

It was shown by X-ray studies that the branching of the macromolecules should affect not only the crystallinity of polyethylene, but also the size of its lattice constants and the density of the crystalline regions. If the degree of branching increases, the unit lattice becomes larger, especially along the axes a and b (Table 3). The length along the c axis (the axis of the macromolecule) of unbranched polyethylene, which is 2.53 Å /53/, remains practically unchanged.

If polyethylene is heated, the unit lattice increases in size, mainly along the a-axis, the length of which attains 7.65 Å at 100°C /48/. It may be said that the effect produced by heating unbranched polyethylene to 100°C is equivalent to that produced by the degree of branching of 40 — 80 CH_3-groups per 1,000 carbon atoms.

7

TABLE 3. Effect of branching on lattice constants /54/

Number of CH$_3$-groups per 1,000 C-atoms	Lattice constants, Å		Density of crystalline fraction of polymer (theoretical), g/cm^3
	a	b	
0	7.36	4.92	1.014
1	7.38	4.95	1.005
3	7.43	4.95	0.999
10	7.52	4.96	0.985
30	7.54	4.97	0.980
40	7.55	4.97	0.979
80	7.68	5.00	0.956

POLYPROPYLENE

Polypropylene is prepared by ionic polymerization on heterogeneous complex catalysts. These catalysts are prepared by reacting compounds of transition metals of Groups IV - VIII in lower valency states (e. g., TiCl$_2$, TiCl$_3$, VCl$_3$) with metal alkyls, alkyl halides or metal hydrides (triethyl-aluminum, diethylaluminum chloride, lithium hydride, etc.).

An important property of the catalysts used in the polymerization of propylene is their crystalline surface, which causes the adsorbed monomer molecules to assume a definite orientation before they combined with the growing polymer chain /55 − 59/. The polymer thus formed may be separated into two fractions which differ in their solubility in hot hydro-carbons (e.g., in heptane). The insoluble crystalline fraction and the soluble amorphous fraction differ in their macromolecular structure. The molecules constituting the crystalline fraction of polypropylene have a regular spatial distribution of the methyl side group with respect to the main chain. On the contrary, the methyl groups in the macromolecular chains of the amorphous fraction are distributed at random. According to the terminology proposed by Natta, polymers with ordered spatial distribution of chain links are called stereoregular, whereas those with a random spatial distribution of the links are called atactic.

The relative contents of the stereoregular and the atactic fraction of polypropylene, which determine to a large extent the properties of the polymer, will depend on the identity of the catalyst and on the conditions of the polymerization. Catalysts on the basis of TiCl$_3$ and an alkylaluminum halide, which contain electron-donating additives such as pyridine, are highly stereospecific and yield a polypropylene which is almost totally crystalline /60/. If the polymerization temperature is decreased, the content of the stereoregular fraction increases.

Two kinds of stereoregular polypropylene may be distinguished: isotactic and syndiotactic. In the former, the methyl groups are situated on one side of the plane of the zigzag-shaped paraffin chain; in the latter, the side groups are located in a perfectly regular alternating sequence on both sides of this plane (Figure 1).

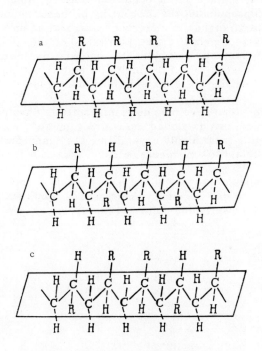

FIGURE 1. Spatial configurations of polypropylene molecules:

a — isotactic; b — syndiotactic; c — atactic.

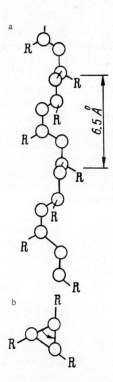

FIGURE 2. Helical structure of a molecule of isotactic polypropylene (a) and its projection onto the plane perpendicular to the axis of the macromolecule (b).

Stereoregular polypropylene displays a marked degree of crystallization. The crystallinity of isotactic polypropylene, which is 60 — 70% /61/, largely depends on its content of the atactic fraction. Inside the crystalline regions each molecule has the form of a helix /62/, in which the angle between the axes of the substituents of contiguous monomeric links is 120°C; the identity period comprises three monomeric links and is 6.5 Å long (Figure 2).

Polypropylene in which isotactic segments alternate with other isotactic segments with the spatial location of the methyl groups opposite to that in the former segments, is also of interest; these are the so-called stereo-block polymers /63/. Depending on the length of the segments of the same type, such materials are more or less elastomeric. If the segments are sufficiently long, partial crystallization takes place. Stereoblock polypropylene is still an elastomer, but displays certain properties of vulcanized elastomer. The crystalline regions, which oppose the creep of the material, exert an effect which is similar to that exerted by the cross-links formed as a result of vulcanization.

The properties of both polyethylene and polypropylene largely depend on their crystallinity and their molecular weight.

Crystallinity depends in the first place on the degree of tacticity, since the chain packing density and, consequently, the probability of formation of a crystalline structure will be much higher in a stereoregular than in an atactic polymer. Crystallinity also depends to a certain extent on the molecular weight: of two equally isotactic polymers, the one with the lower molecular weight may be more crystalline. If the melt of a highly isotactic polymer is rapidly cooled, the resulting solid material may have a low degree of crystallinity.

The crystallinity of a polypropylene specimen determines all its physical properties. If the degree of isotacticity is varied, an entire gamut of materials can be obtained, ranging from highly crystalline, stiff, mechanically strong and chemically resistant to amorphous, elastic, heat-sensitive polymers.

The properties of different types of polypropylene have been described /63, 64/. We shall merely mention that polypropylene typically combines mechanical strength, stiffness, high softening point and low density:

Main parameters of polypropylene

Density, g/cm^3	0.90—0.91
Melting point, °C	167—170
Brittleness temperature, °C	−10 to +20
Tensile strength, kg/cm^2	300—400
Elongation at break, %, not more than	1,000
Flexural modulus, kg/cm^2	8,000—12,000
Vicat softening temperature, °C	145—155
Water absorption, %	0.01—0.03
Dielectric constant at $5 \cdot 10^7$ sec^{-1}	2.2
Electric volume resistivity, ohm·cm	$3 \cdot 10^{16} - 8 \cdot 10^{16}$

The drawbacks of polypropylene include embrittlement at low temperatures and poor resistance to oxidants, heat and UV radiation.

POLYMERS OF HIGHER α-OLEFINS

The organometallic catalyst complexes utilized in the polymerization of ethylene and propylene can also be employed to prepare polymers of higher α-olefins, in particular those of butene-1, 3-methylbutene-1 and 4-methylpentene-1, which are likely to find practical applications. These polyolefins display high degrees of crystallinity, which vary with the conditions of the synthesis. The macromolecules comprised within crystalline regions have a helical structure.

In macromolecules of isotactic polybutene-1, as in molecules of polypropylene, each turn of the helix (identity period 6.5 Å /65/) contains three monomeric links. As the size of the substituents increases, the identity period becomes larger and the configuration of the helix becomes more involved. The identity period in the helical structure of isotactic poly-3-methylbutene-1 is 6.84 Å, while that of poly-4-methylpentene-1 is 13.85 Å /66/.

Isotactic polybutene-1 resembles low-pressure polyethylene in its properties /67 — 69/:

Main parameters of polybutene-1

Density, g/cm^3	0.912
Melt index, g/10 min	0.5
Melting point, °C	135
Brittleness temperature, °C	−25
Tensile strength, kg/cm^2	270
Yield point, kg/cm^2	155
Elongation at break, %	350
Elasticity modulus, kg/cm^2	18,200
Vicat softening temperature, °C	113
Dielectric constant at 10^6 sec^{-1}	2.2

An important typical property of polybutene-1 is its high creep resistance between −25°C (brittleness temperature) and +90°C. Polybutene-1 is also very resistant to cracking produced by internal strains, external loads and surface-active agents.

Polypentene-1 has a limited resistance to heat; the melting point of the isotactic polymer is 80°C /55/.

Polymerization of next higher members of α-olefin series (hexene-1, etc.) yields rubberlike products.

The relationship between the melting point and the length of the side chains in isotactic poly-α-olefins is shown in Figure 3. Between polypropylene and higher α-olefins up to $C_7 — C_9$ the melting point decreases owing to the increasingly imperfect packing in the helix /65, 70 — 72/. The increase in the melting point between polydecene-1 and polyoctadecene-1 is probably due to the improved packing of the side chains as their length increases /70/.

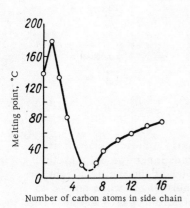

FIGURE 3. Melting point of polyolefins as a function of the side chain length /70/.

Highly heat-resistant polymers are obtained by polymerization of the monomers 3-methylbutene-1 and 4-methylpentene-1, which form branched macromolecules. The melting point of the crystalline poly-3-methylbutene-1 is 245°C /66/ (or about 310°C /73/), while the melting point of crystalline poly-4-methylpentene-1 has been reported as 205°C /66/ and about 240°C /73/.

Poly-4-methylpentene-1 is prepared by polymerization of 4-methyl-pentene-1 in the presence of organometallic catalysts, e.g., complexes between alkylaluminum compounds or alkylaluminum halides and titanium or vanadium halides, under conditions similar to those employed in the polymerization of ethylene or propylene. It has been shown /74/ that the polymerization of tertiary amines is catalyzed by the catalyst system

11

triethylaluminum — titanium trichloride. It is known /75/ that 4-methyl-pentene-1 becomes polymerized in the presence of an oxide of a metal capable of forming a halide and an organic compound with not less than two halogen atoms at the same carbon atom, say, a mixture of aluminum oxide with carbon tetrachloride. Another catalyst system which may be employed is a halide of a metal of Group IV - VI and an organosilicon compound, e.g., a mixture of $TiCl_3$ and $TiCl_4$ with phenylsiloxane /76/.

Poly-4-methylpentene-1 displays a specific combination of several valuable properties /77 — 80/. The values of various parameters of the polymer prepared in the presence of the last-named catalyst system are shown below:

Properties of poly-4-methylpentene-1 /77/

Density, g/cm^3	0.83
Melting point, °C	240
Tensile strength, kg/cm^2	
at 20°C	280
at 100°C	70
Elongation at break, %	50
Elasticity modulus on extension at 20°C, kg/cm^2	11,000
Vicat softening temperature, °C	179
Linear expansion coefficient, $degree^{-1}$	$11.5 \cdot 10^{-5}$
Dielectric loss factor at 10^3 Hz	0.00015
Dielectric constant at 25°C	2.12
Electric volume resistivity, ohm·cm, not less than . . .	10^{16}

Poly-4-methylpentene-1 is the lightest plastic material known; its density is only 0.83 g/cm^3. It is almost as transparent as poly (methyl methacrylate), transmitting as it does about 90% of the incident light. Articles produced from this polymer retain their shape when heated to 200°C. The polymer is somewhat more permeable to gases and to water than other polyolefins, such as polyethylene or polypropylene.

Polymers of the optically active higher α-olefins (3-methylpentene-1, 4-methylhexene-1, 4-methylheptene-1, 5-methylheptene-1, 6-methyloctene-1, etc.) are also optically active /81 — 85/.

Bibliography

1. Chem. Techn. — 17 (7): 434. 1965.
2. Kunststoff-Berater.— 10 (9): 717. 1965.
3. Kem. Ind., 13 (10): 839. 1964.
4. Raff, R. A. V. and J. B. Allison. Polyethylene. — Interscience, N. Y.—L. 1956.
5. Renfrew, A. and P. Morgan (editors). Polythene: The Technology and Uses of Ethylene Polymers. — New York, Interscience. 2nd ed. 1960.

6. Shifrina, V.S. and N.N. Samosatskii. Polietilen (Polyethylene). — Goskhimizdat. 1961.

7. Hagen, H. and H. Domininhaus. Polyäthylene und andere Polyolefine. — Hamburg, Verlag Brunke Garrels. 1961.

8. Golding, B. Polymers and Resins: their Chemistry and Chemical Engineering. — Princeton, New Jersey, Van Nostrand. 1959.

9. Nikolaev, A.F. Sinteticheskie polimery i plasticheskie massy na ikh osnove (Synthetic Polymers and Resins Formed from Them). — Izdatel'stvo "Khimiya." 1967.

10. Khuvink, R. and A. Staverman. Khimiya i tekhnologiya polimerov (The Chemistry and Technology of Polymers). Vol. 2, Part 1. — Izdatel'stvo "Khimiya." 1965.

11. Hunter, E. In: Polythene (edited by A. Renfrew and P. Morgan), pp. 43 — 68. — New York, Interscience. 1960.

12. Danby, C.J. and C.N. Hinshelwood. — Proc. Roy. Soc., 179A: 169. 1942.

13. Landers, L.C. and D.H. Volman. — J. Am. Chem. Soc., 79: 2996. 1957.

14. Roedel, M.J. — J. Am. Chem. Soc., 76 (24): 6110. 1953.

15. Willbourn, A.H. — J. Polymer Sci., 34: 369. 1959.

16. Sirota, A.G., E.P. Ryabikov, A.L. Goldenberg, P.A. Il'chenko, and L.F. Chopko. — Plastmassy, No. 11: 5. 1965.

17. Goldenberg, A.L., V.M. Zapletnik, and P.A. Il'chenko. — In: "Spektroskopiya polimerov," Kiev, Izdatel'stvo "Naukova Dumka." 1967.

18. Ballantine, D.S. and B. Manowitz. — Nucl. Sci. Abs., 7: 3730. 1953.

19. Lewis, J.G., J.J. Martin, and L.C. Anderson. — Chem. Eng. Progr., 50: 249. 1954.

20. Hayword, J.H. and R.H. Bretton. — Chem. Eng. Progr., 50: 73. 1954.

21. Laird, R.K., A.G. Morell, and L. Seed. — Disc. Faraday Soc., 22: 126. 1956.

22. Bugaenko, L.T., T.S. Nikitina, A.N. Pravodnikov, and Yu. M. Malinskii. Khimicheskoe deistvie ioniziruyushchikh izluchenii (The Chemical Action of Ionizing Radiation). — VINITI. 1958.

23. Munari, S., G. Gastello, S. Russo, and C. Rossi. — Chim. Ind. Milan, 47 (1): 20. 1965.

24. Natta, G. — Experienta Suppl., 7: 21. 1957.

25. Julia, M. — Compt. rend., 245: 70. 1957.

26. Bawn, C.E.H. In: Polythene (edited by A. Renfew and P. Morgan). — New York, Interscience. 1960.

27. Polietilen nizkogo davleniya (Low-Pressure Polyethylene), edited by N.M. Egorov. — Goskhimizdat. 1960.

28. Belgian Patent 533362. 1955.

29. Burch, G.N., G.B. Field, F.A. McTigue, and H.M. Spurlin. — SPE J., 13 (5): 34. 1957.

30. GFR Patent 1182827. 1964.

31. GFR Patent 1183245. 1964.

32. Belgian Patent 530617. 1955.

33. Belgian Patent 535082. 1955.

34. Polietilen srednego davleniya (Medium-Pressure Polyethylene).
    edited by S. V. Shchutskii. — Izdatel'stvo "Khimiya." 1965.
35. US Patent 2658059. 1953.
36. US Patent 2692261. 1954.
37. US Patent 2692295. 1954.
38. British Patent 721046. 1954.
39. US Patent 2717888. 1955.
40. US Patent 2717889. 1955.
41. Clark, A. and J. P. Hogan. In: Polythene (edited by A. Renfrew and
    P. Morgan), pp. 29 — 34. — New York, Interscience. 1960.
42. d'Ouville, E. L. In: Polythene (edited by A. Renfrew and P. Morgan),
    pp. 35 — 42. — New York, Interscience. 1960.
43. Clark, A. and P. Hogan. — Ind. Eng. Chem., 48 (7): 1152. 1956.
44. Arkhipova, Z. V., A. S. Semenova, M. G. Zhbankova,
    A. G. Sirota, and E. N. Nalivaiko. — Plastmassy, No. 1:
    17. 1959.
45. Ermakov, Yu. I., G. K. Boreskov, V. A. Dzis'ko, and L. I.
    Ivanova. — Doklady AN SSSR, 145 (4): 787. 1962.
46. Gol'denberg, A. L. and S. G. Lyubetskii. — Vysokomolekularnye
    Soedineniya, No. 6: 905, 1963.
47. Smith, D. C. — Ind. Eng. Chem., 48 (7): 1161. 1956.
48. Gaylord, N. G. and H. F. Mark. Linear and Stereoregular Addition
    Polymers. — New York, Interscience. 1959.
49. Rekasheva, A. F. and A. A. Kiprianova. — Vysokomolekulyarnye
    Soedineniya, 3: 1446. 1961.
50. Curphey, E. C. — Brit. Plast., 31: 63. 1958.
51. Richards, R. B. — J. Appl. Chem., 1: 370. 1951.
52. Bunn, C. W. In: Polythene (edited by A. Renfrew and P. Morgan),
    pp. 87 — 130. — New York, Interscience. 1960.
53. Bunn, C. W. — Trans. Faraday Soc., 35: 482. 1939.
54. Walter, E. R. and F. P. Reding. — J. Polymer Sci., 21 (99): 561.
    1956.
55. Natta, G. — Makromol. Chem., 16: 213. 1955.
56. Natta, G., P. Pino, and P. Moraglio. — J. Am. Chem. Soc.,
    77: 1708. 1955.
57. Natta, G. — J. Polymer Sci., 16: 143. 1956.
58. Natta, G., G. Mazzanti, G. Crespi, and G. Moraglio. —
    Chim. Ind., Milan, 39 (4): 275. 1957.
59. Bresler, S. E. and B. L. Erusalimskii. Fizika i khimiya
    makromolekul (The Physics and Chemistry of Macromolecules),
    p. 411. — Izdatel'stvo "Nauka." 1965.
60. Natta, G., J. Pasquon, and Y. Gatti. — J. Polymer Sci.,
    51: 387. 1961.
61. Coppel, J. M. — Brit. Plast., 32 (5): 207. 1959.
62. Natta, G. and P. Corradini. — J. Polymer Sci., 34: 529. 1959.
63. Kresser, T. Polypropylene. — New York, Reinhold. 1960.
64. Rovner, J. Polipropilen (Polypropylene), edited by V. I. Pilipovskii
    and I. K. Yartsev, p. 95. — Izdatel'stvo "Khimiya." 1967.
65. Natta, G., P. Corradini, and J. W. Bassi. — Makromol. Chem.,
    21: 240. 1956.
66. Natta, G. — Angew. Chem., 68: 393. 1955.

67. Hinds, L. — Rubb. J. Internat. Plastics, 138 (11): 382. 1960.
68. Pract. Plast., 11 (6): 29. 1960.
69. Chem. Eng. News, 38 (1): 24. 1960.
70. Turner, J. A. — Makromol. Chem., 71: 1. 1964.
71. Natta, G. and P. Corradini. — Makromol. Chem., 16: 213. 1955.
72. Natta, G., P. Corradini, and M. Cesari. — Atti Accad. Linc.,
       21: 365. 1956.
73. Campbell, T. W. and A. C. Haven. — J. Appl. Polymer Sci.,
       1: 79. 1959.
74. British Patent 886093. 1962.
75. Belgian Patent 632378.
76. British Patent 934119. 1963.
77. Beduneau, H. — Rev. prod. chim., 69 (1341): 9. 1966.
78. Rubber Plastics Age, 46 (4): 415. 1965.
79. Rubber Plastics Age, 46 (5): 499. 1965.
80. Brit. Plastics, 38 (4): 213. 1965.
81. Pino, P., G. P. Lorenzi, and L. Lardicci. — J. Polymer Sci.,
       53: 340. 1961.
82. Bayley, W. J. and E. T. Yates. — J. Org. Chem., 25: 1800. 1960.
83. Nozakura, S., S. Takeuchi, H. Yuki, and S. Murahashi. —
       Bull. Chem. Soc. Japan, 34: 1673. 1961.
84. Goodman, M., K. G. Clarke, M. A. Stake, and A. Abe. —
       Makromol. Chem., 72: 131. 1964.
85. Goodman, M., J. Braudrup, and H. F. Mark. — High Polymers,
       20: 1, Crystalline Olefin Polymers, p. 91. — New York, Interscience.
       1965.

Chapter II

COPOLYMERS OF α-OLEFINS

COPOLYMERS OF ETHYLENE WITH PROPYLENE
AND OTHER α-OLEFINS

One of the most important techniques for the modification of the structure and properties of polyethylene is its copolymerization with propylene, α-butylene or other α-olefins when branched links are introduced into the main polymer chain.

As a result of having a branched structure, the structure of these copolymers is less ordered than that of polyethylene itself. Accordingly, copolymerization with α-olefins is chiefly used to modify the structure of highly ordered polyethylene (low-pressure and medium-pressure polyethylene); however, ethylene may also be copolymerized with, say, α-butylene, propylene or octene-1 by free radical mechanism /1/.

By varying the content of the comonomer in the ethylene it is possible to prepare a wide range of materials which differ from one another, mainly by the properties which are related to the degree of ordering of the structure. Copolymers of ethylene with α-olefins are also of interest as model compounds /2, 3/ in the study of the relation between the structure of the macromolecule and formation of supermolecular structures. Their value as model compounds consists in the fact that practically all their branches are identical, and the number of the branches can be varied and can be determined.

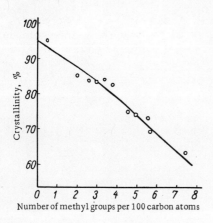

FIGURE 4. Degree of crystallinity of copolymers of ethylene with propylene as a function of the number of methyl side groups /4/.

The most important result of the introduction of comonomer links into the macromolecules of polyethylene is that the latter become more amorphous. As the number of comonomer links with branching points in the copolymer increases, the crystallinity decreases. As an example, Figure 4 shows the crystallinity of ethylene copolymers with propylene, prepared on a chromium oxide catalyst, as a function of the content of methyl groups in the side chains /4/.

Curves giving the scattering intensities of X-rays as a function of the scattering angle, which are used to estimate the degree of crystallinity, show not only a decrease in crystallinity, but also a shift in the diffraction curve (Figure 5), which shows that the interplanar distance has increased /4/. The increase in the size of the unit lattice takes place mainly along the a-axis and, to a smaller extent, along the b-axis as well (Figure 6, Table 4), while the distance c remains practically unchanged.

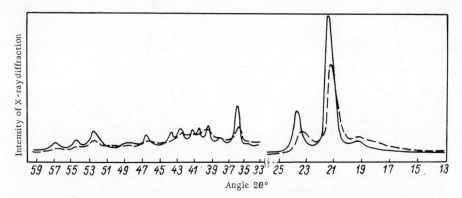

FIGURE 5. X-ray diffraction curves of polyethylene (———) and of the copolymer of ethylene with propylene (7.5 CH$_3$-groups per 100 carbon atoms) (------), prepared on chromium oxide catalyst /4/.

TABLE 4. Lattice constants of copolymers of ethylene with α-olefins /5/

Comonomer	Comonomer content, mole %	Lattice constants, Å	
		a	b
Butene-1	3.6	7.521	4.964
Pentene-1	3.1	7.474	4.969
Hexene-1	3.4	7.467	4.965
Heptene-1	1.4	7.479	4.956

The crystallinity of ethylene copolymers depends, first and foremost, on the content of the comonomer. For a given content of the copolymer, the degree of crystallinity is also a function of the hydrocarbon chain length of the comonomer /3, 6/. Figure 7 represents the crystallinity of copolymers of medium-pressure ethylene as a function of the number of carbon atoms in the molecule of α-olefin. As the chain length of the comonomer (and thus also the length of the side branches) increases, the crystallinity decreases and attains a minimum value if $C_4 - C_6$ α-olefins are employed as comonomers. Further increase in the chain length of the α-olefin does not significantly reduce the crystallinity and may even increase it somewhat. The probable reason for it is that a side chain containing $4-5$ or more carbon atoms is sufficiently long and sufficiently flexible to become oriented along the main chain. Such long branchings may be expected to be located in the crystalline regions of the copolymers. A similar conclusion was arrived at by Swan /5/, who studied the variation in the size of the unit lattice of copolymers of ethylene with higher α-olefins (Table 4).

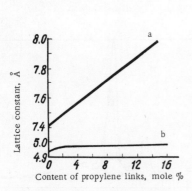

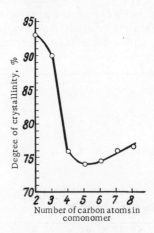

FIGURE 6. Lattice constants of co-polymers of ethylene with propylene as a function of the content of propylene links /5/.

FIGURE 7. Degree of crystallinity of copolymers of ethylene as a function of the length of comono-mer chain. The content of the comonomer in the copolymer is constant at 2.1 ± 0.4 mole %. The experimental point marked on the ordinate axis indicates medium-pressure polyethylene /3/.

Associates of crystalline formations (spherulites) in copolymers are smaller and less well developed than in polyethylene (Figure 8).

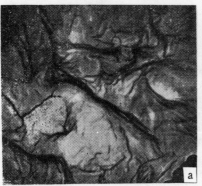

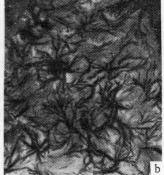

FIGURE 8. Electron microphotographs of polyethylene (a) and of a copolymer of ethylene with propylene (b), containing 75 methyl groups per 1,000 carbon atoms (crystallization from solutions in xylene). × 10,000 /4/.

The low crystallinity of copolymers of ethylene, as compared with low-pressure and medium-pressure homopolymers of ethylene, is also reflected in the lower densities of the former (Figure 9). If the crystallinity of the copolymer is varied by introducing variable amounts of the comonomer, materials with different elasticity moduli can be prepared (Figure 10).

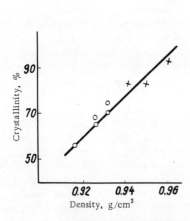

FIGURE 9. Relationship between the degree of crystallinity and density of a copolymer of ethylene with propylene /7/:

O — low-pressure copolymer of ethylene with propylene; ● — high-pressure polyethylene; × — low-pressure polyethylene.

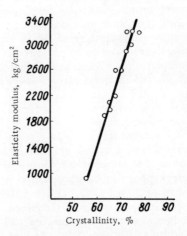

FIGURE 10. Elasticity modulus of low-pressure copolymers of ethylene with propylene as a function of the crystallinity /7/.

Such copolymers are less liable to crack under the effect of internal strains, external stresses or surface-active media than low-pressure and medium-pressure polyethylene. The resistance of the copolymers to cracking is in agreement with data obtained by electron-microscopic studies of their structure /9/ and by studies of the growth of crystalline copolymer formations in polyethylene, which show that a reduction in the supermolecular degree of ordering increases the resistance of the material to cracking.

Since the degree of crystallinity of copolymers is low and their crystalline formations are imperfect, their resistance to heat is relatively low. Table 5 shows the softening points of copolymers of ethylene with propylene, prepared on chromium oxide catalyst from gas mixtures containing ethylene and propylene components in different ratios. As the propylene content increases, the softening point of the copolymer decreases and the density decreases as well.

Thus it is seen that the main differences between copolymers of ethylene with higher α-olefins and low-pressure and medium-pressure polyethylene are the consequence of the higher degree of branching of the copolymers and of the lower degree of ordering of the supermolecular structure. The main differences are higher density and stiffness values and somewhat lower softening points. Such copolymers display elasticity in conjunction with high dielectric properties and chemical inertness, and can be injection-molded and extruded; they are accordingly valuable materials for the manufacture of electric cables, films and other articles which cannot be made of high-density polyethylene owing to its excessive stiffness.

Ethylene copolymers with propylene and with α-butylene are the copolymers most frequently employed in industry /2 — 5, 10 — 24/.

Copolymerizations catalyzed by metal oxides are effected under conditions very similar to those employed in the polymerization of ethylene. The usual practice is to use mixtures of ethylene with a small amount of the comonomer. Thus, the concentration of propylene never exceeds 20 vol. %, and is most often between 3 and 10 vol. % /25 — 27/. This is because of the considerable deterioration in the mechanical strength of ethylene copolymers formed from mixtures containing large proportions of the comonomer.

The copolymerization is effected using a mixture of the desired composition in a hydrocarbon solvent (decalin, benzene, heptane, toluene, isooctane). If supported chromium oxide catalyst, say, on aluminum silicate support is employed, the process is realized under 30 — 40 atm pressure at 90 — 130°C. Other catalysts which can also be employed include oxides of other metals of Groups V and VI on supports, in particular molybdenum oxides on alumina /28 — 32/, vanadium oxides on alumina /33, 34/ and on silica gel /35 — 37/ and tungsten oxides on zirconium oxide /38 — 41/. Such catalysts are activated by hydrogen at 350 — 480°C and are mainly used in the presence of accelerators (sodium and calcium hydrides, sodium hydroxide, metallic sodium, lithium aluminum hydride, lithium borohydride). The copolymerization is then realized at 150 — 240°C, under a pressure of 35 — 70 atm.

TABLE 5. Properties of copolymers of ethylene with propylene prepared at various monomer ratios /8/

C_2/C_3 weight ratio	Softening point, °C	Density, g/cm^3	Molecular weight
100/0	121	0.960	29,500
95/5	117	0.948	27,900
90/10	115	0.938	25,200
85/15	114	0.937	30,900
80/20	113	0.932	26,000

Homopolymerization of propylene and next higher α-olefins is slow (e. g., propylene, 10 g/g·hr; hexene-1, 8 g/g·hr /22/), but the rate of copolymerization of ethylene with these monomers is fast — almost as fast as the homopolymerization rate of ethylene (1,000 g/g·hr) /22, 24/.

The copolymerization temperature largely determines the properties of the final product. At high temperatures the intrinsic viscosity of the copolymers decreases (Figure 11) and the mechanical properties deteriorate. The structure and properties of the products obtained by medium-pressure copolymerization is adjusted, more often than not, by varying the proportions of the initial monomer components. Increased content of the comonomer in the initial mixture with ethylene results in increased branching (Figure 12) and a lower crystallinity of the copolymer.

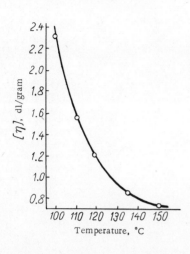

FIGURE 11.   Intrinsic viscosity of copolymers of ethylene with propylene as
a function of copolymerization temperature. Content of propylene in mixture
with ethylene: 10%. Chromium oxide
catalyst /20/.

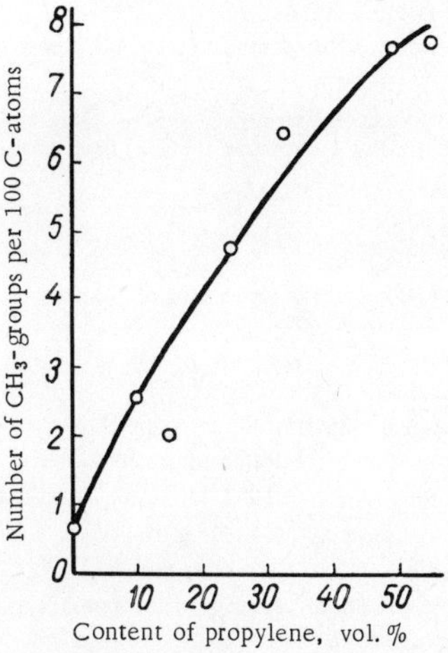

FIGURE 12.   Degree of branching of
medium-pressure copolymers as a
function of the content of propylene
in ethylene-propylene mixture /20/.

The content of double bonds in copolymers is close to that which is typical of medium-pressure polyethylene (Table 1). The unsaturated groups in the copolymer macromolecules are mainly terminal vinyl groups.

Unsaturation of medium-pressure ethylene-propylene copolymer
(25 methyl groups per 1,000 carbon atoms) /20/

Number of $>C=C<$ groups per 1,000 C atoms . . . .   1.0—1.1

Contents of individual groups, %:

terminal vinyl $\begin{smallmatrix}H\\R'\end{smallmatrix}>C=CH_2$ 65

side vinylidene $\begin{smallmatrix}R\\R'\end{smallmatrix}>C=CH_2$ 21

internal trans-vinylene $\begin{smallmatrix}H\\R'\end{smallmatrix}C=C\begin{smallmatrix}R'\\H\end{smallmatrix}$ 14

The values of the main physical and mechanical parameters of medium-pressure copolymers (density, mechanical strength, resistance to heat, elasticity modulus, water absorption) are intermediate between those of high-pressure and medium-pressure polyethylene (Table 2):

Main parameters of medium-pressure ethylene-propylene copolymers /20/

Intrinsic viscosity in decalin at 135°C, dl/g	1.0—2.5
Number of methyl groups per 1,000 carbon atoms	15—30
Crystallinity, %	75—80
Density, g/cm^3	0.94—0.95
Melting point, °C	114—125
Brittleness temperature, °C, not higher than	−70
Tensile strength, kg/cm^2	140—220
Elongation at break, %	150—800
Flexural modulus, kg/cm^2	3,000—6,000
Brinell hardness, kg/mm^2.	1.3—2.6
Water absorption during 30 days, at 20°C, %	0.01—0.02
Dielectric loss factor at 10^6 sec^{-1}, not more than.	$4 \cdot 10^{-4}$
Dielectric constant at 10^6 sec^{-1}	2.3
Electric volume resistivity, ohm·cm	10^{17}
AC dielectric strength, specimen thickness 2 mm	28—30

The structure and properties of ethylene-propylene copolymer differ from those of ethylene—α-butylene copolymer even when both copolymers contain an equal number of comonomer links /11/. In accordance with the data given above concerning the effect of the length of the side chain on crystallinity, ethyl side chains impair the crystalline structure much more strongly than do methyl side chains (Figure 13). Accordingly, if the two copolymers are to have the same degree of crystallinity, the content of α-butylene in the initial mixture with ethylene should be smaller than that of propylene (Figure 14).

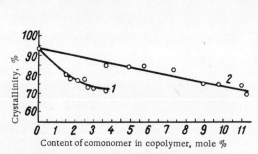

FIGURE 13. Degree of crystallinity as a function of the composition of copolymers of ethylene with α-butylene (1) and with propylene (2), prepared on chromium oxide catalyst /20/.

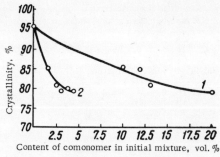

FIGURE 14. Degree of crystallinity of copolymers of ethylene with propylene (1) and with α-butylene (2) prepared on chromium oxide catalyst, as a function of the composition of the initial monomer mixture /20/.

A comparison of the properties of ethylene — α-butylene copolymer with those of polyethylene (Table 6) shows that the copolymer is much more stable to cracking and has a larger elongation at break; on the other hand, its tensile strength, stiffness and softening point values are inferior to those of polyethylene. Nevertheless, its softening point is high enough to withstand steam sterilization of commercial articles at 121°C during 20 minutes.

TABLE 6. Physical and mechanical properties of a copolymer of ethylene with α-butylene and polyethylene /19/

Parameter	Copolymer with density 0.95 g/cm³				Polyethylene with density 0.96 g/cm³			
Melt index, g/10 min . . .	0.3	1.2	4.0	6.5	0.2	0.9	3.5	5.0
Tensile strength, kg/cm² .	250	250	250	250	310	310	310	310
Stiffness modulus, kg/cm² .	8,050	8,050	8,050	8,050	10,500	10,500	10,500	10,500
Vicat softening point, °C. .	124	124	124	124	127	127	127	127
Shore hardness, Scale D . .	67	67	67	67	68	68	68	68
Cracking in surfactant, hours	400	70	20	10	64	14	2	1
Brittleness point, °C	−118	−118	−107	−96	−118	−118	−103	−73

Copolymerizations of ethylene with more than one α-olefin are also of interest /3, 42/. Thus, for instance, $C_5 - C_7$ α-olefins, contained in the $27 - 95°C$ fraction of the product of high-speed catalytic cracking of soft paraffin /43/, could be copolymerized with ethylene on a chromium oxide catalyst. This fraction contained 52% heptene-1, 17% hexene-1, 4% pentene-1, as well as some pentane, hexane and heptane. The degree of crystallinity and related properties (tensile strength, elasticity modulus, melting point, etc.) of copolymers of ethylene with higher α-olefin mixtures are intermediate between those of medium-pressure and high-pressure polyethylene:

Main parameters of medium-pressure copolymer of ethylene with $C_5 - C_7$ α-olefin mixture

Intrinsic viscosity in decalin at 135°C, dl/g	1.0−3.0
Number of CH_3-groups per 1,000 C-atoms	10−21
Crystallinity, %	75−80
Density, g/cm³.	0.92−0.95
Melting point, °C	113−128
Tensile strength, kg/cm²	170−220
Flexural modulus, kg/cm²	4,200−6,500

These copolymers are very stable to cracking under the action of surfactant media and prolonged application of loads. When specimens of these copolymers were tested under tension in 5% aqueous solution of the emulsifying agent OP-10 at 80°C by a method resembling that recommended by ASTM /44/, no cracking was observed up to 56 hours' exposure. Specimens of medium-pressure polyethylene cracked within 9 hours under the same conditions of testing.

Of the ethylene copolymers prepared on organometallic complex catalysts, ethylene-propylene copolymers have been studied in most detail and are the most extensively used. The ratio between the number of ethylene to propylene links in copolymerization products may vary widely. If the propylene content is up to $15-20\%$, the copolymers are highly crystalline and display the properties of plastomers /45, 7/:

Main properties of ethylene-propylene copolymers prepared under low pressure (propylene content less than 20 mole %) /7/

Weight-average molecular weight . . . . $100,000-500,000$
Intrinsic viscosity in decalin at $135°C$, dl/g . . . . $1.5-4.2$
Melt index (load 5 kg, capillary diameter 2 mm), g/10 min . . . . $0.6-0.05$
Methyl groups per 1,000 carbon atoms . . . . $70-20$

Number of $>C = C<$ groups per 1,000 C-atoms . . . . $0.3-0.4$

Content of groups, %:

terminal vinyl $\overset{H}{\underset{R}{>}}C = CH_2$ 30

side vinylidene $\overset{R}{\underset{R'}{>}}C = CH_2$ 30

internal trans-vinylene $\overset{H}{\underset{R}{>}}C = C\overset{R'}{\underset{H}{<}}$ 40

Crystallinity, % . . . . $55-75$
Density, g/cm . . . . $0.917-0.937$
Melting point, °C . . . . $109-126$
Tensile strength (extension rate 100 mm/min), kg/cm^2 . . . . $170-320$
Flexural strength, kg/cm^2 . . . . $170-200$
Yield strength, kg/cm^2 . . . . $80-160$
Elongation at break, % . . . . $500-900$
Flexural modulus, kg/cm^2 . . . . $900-3,300$
Dielectric loss factor at $10^6 sec^{-1}$ . . . . $2 \cdot 10^{-4}-6 \cdot 10^{-4}$
Dielectric constant at $10^6 sec^{-1}$ . . . . $2.2-2.3$
Electric volume resistivity, ohm·cm . . . . 10^{17}
AC dielectric strength (thickness of specimen 2 mm), kV/mm . . . . $30-36$

If the proportion of propylene is high, the copolymers are amorphous and are typical elastomers. These products form the subject of numerous publications, in particular those by Natta et al. /46-51/. The synthesis, structure and properties of rubberlike copolymers of ethylene with propylene and the manufacture of rubbers based on these materials were reviewed in detail by Seidov /52/.

The copolymerization of ethylene with propylene on complex organometallic catalysts resembles low-pressure polymerization of ethylene. It is most often realized under pressures of less than 10 atm and at temperatures not exceeding $80-100°C$ in saturated hydrocarbon solvents or in liquid propylene /53 — 62/. If the concentration of ethylene in liquid propylene is changed, the resulting copolymers contain between 5 and 60% of propylene links. The reaction is catalyzed by products of interaction between alkylaluminum compounds or alkylaluminum halides and chlorides or other salts of vanadium or titanium. If it is desired to prepare elastomers, vanadium catalysts are to be preferred, since these yield amorphous products of uniform structure. If titanium catalysts are employed, the product will be partly crystalline even if the content of propylene in the initial mixture with ethylene is large /63/.

The mutual proportions of ethylene and propylene in the reaction mixture are the principal factor which determines the composition of the final product. Figure 15 shows the composition of the copolymer as a function of the monomer concentration ratio. It is seen from the figure that ethylene is much more active in the copolymerization than is propylene. The low activity of propylene during copolymerization which takes place by an anionic mechanism is connected with the electron-donating nature of the methyl group in the propylene molecule.

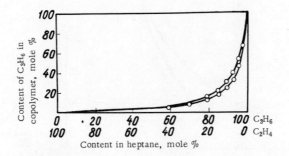

FIGURE 15. Effect of ethylene/propylene concentration ratio on the composition of copolymers (vanadium catalyst, heptane solvent, 30°C, 1 atm) /63/.

As distinct from the rate constants of free radical copolymerizations, which are independent of the nature of the catalysts and depend only on the structure of the comonomers, the constants of copolymerizations conducted on complex organometallic catalysts depend on the nature of the catalyst. In particular, the values of the copolymerization constants vary strongly for different transition metal halides in the catalyst (Table 7).

TABLE 7. Copolymerization constants of ethylene with propylene on various catalyst systems

Catalyst system	r C_2H_4	r C_3H_6	References
$VCl_4 + Al(C_6H_{13})_3$	7.08	0.088	/46/
$VCl_3 + Al(C_5H_{13})_3$	5.61	0.145	/47/
$VOCl_3 + Al(C_6H_{13})_3$	17.95	0.065	/45/
$TiCl_4 + Al(C_6H_{13})_3$	33.36	0.032	/48/
$TiCl_3 + Al(C_6H_{13})_3$	15.72	0.11	/48/

25

Figure 16 shows the effect of the catalyst used on the composition of copolymers at different component ratios of ethylene to propylene in the initial mixture.

In studying the different catalyst systems, it should be borne in mind that, in accordance with the theory of copolymerization, the alternation of the comonomer links is related to the copolymerization constants. The smaller the product of the copolymerization constants, the smaller the probability of formation of blocks of identical monomer links in the copolymer chain. If the alternation of the links is such that homogeneous blocks are not formed, the resulting copolymers will clearly be amorphous.

If the content of propylene links is 30 mole % or higher, the copolymers will be almost totally amorphous (Figure 17), but if the propylene content of copolymers is too high, they will be less elastic /51, 52/. If the propylene content is more than 60%, the copolymers vitrify at higher temperatures (Figure 18). Copolymers containing 30 − 40% propylene are usually employed as rubbers /64/.

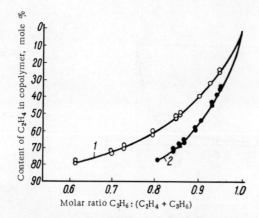

FIGURE 16. Composition of copolymers as a function of ethylene-to-propylene ratio in the reaction medium (liquid phase copolymerization on different catalyst systems) /51/:

1 − VCl₃ + Al(C₆H₁₃)₃; 2 − TiCl₃ + Al(C₆H₁₃)₃.

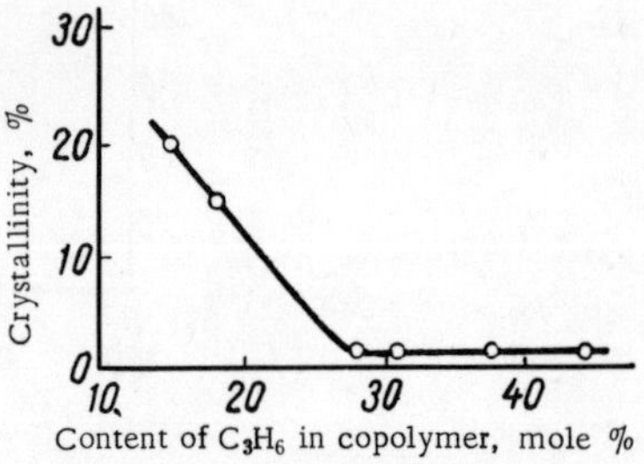

FIGURE 17. Crystallinity of ethylene copolymers with propylene as a function of their composition /61/.

Of the elastomers other than ethylene-propylene copolymers, copolymers of ethylene with α-butylene are of potential practical interest /51, p. 275; 54, 65 − 69/. The copolymerization constants of ethylene and α-butylene were determined by Natta et al. /65/, who used vanadium catalysts (Table 8).

The experimental conditions and the relationships governing copolymerization of ethylene with α-butylene are the same as for the copolymerization of ethylene with propylene.

Ternary copolymers of ethylene, propylene and α-butylene are known /51, p. 279; 70/. If the proportion of ethylene links is less than 75%, the copolymers are fully amorphous and are elastic; they resemble ethylene-propylene elastomers.

TABLE 8. Constants of copolymerization of ethylene with α-butylene /65/

Catalyst system	$r C_2H_7$	$r C_4H_8$
$VCl_4 + (C_6H_{13})_3Al$	29.60	0.019
$VCl_3 + (C_6H_{13})_3Al$	29.96	0.043

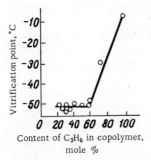

FIGURE 18. Vitrification point of ethylene-propylene copolymers as a function of their composition /52/.

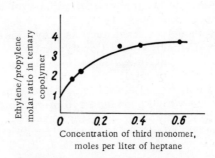

FIGURE 19. Composition of copolymer as a function of the concentration of the third monomer (cyclooctadiene) in the reaction mixture /52/.

The preparation of elastomers by copolymerization of ethylene with pentene-1 in liquid pentene-1 has been described /52/.

Since there are no unsaturated groups in the rubberlike ethylene copolymers, sulfur cannot be used as vulcanization (cross-linking) agent. The conventional vulcanization methods become applicable if a small amount (1 – 3% of the total number of links) of a third monomer, containing two or more double bonds, is introduced into the copolymer of ethylene with propylene or with another α-olefin /52, 71 – 99/.

Such third monomers may be aliphatic or cyclic dienes, mostly with unconjugated double bonds, but conjugated dienes have also been used: isoprene, butadiene-1,3, pentadiene-1,3 /76, 81/. Cyclic dienes which have been employed for the purpose include dicyclopentadiene, cyclo-heptadiene, cyclooctadiene, vinylcyclohexene-3, divinylcyclobutane, etc. /52/.

The most suitable aliphatic dienes are those in which the two double bonds display differing activities, with one bond in the α-position and the other in the interior of the molecule. Examples of such compounds are hexadiene-1,4 or heptadiene-1,5. During the copolymerization the more active double bonds in the α-position will open, while the internal double bonds will remain in the side chains of the copolymer and will thus render vulcanization possible. It is less desirable to use dienes with both double bonds in the α-position, since during the copolymerization both double bonds may open.

The synthesis of ternary copolymers is realized under the same conditions as the copolymerization of ethylene with propylene. It was shown that the introduction of the diene into the reaction mixture affects the ratio between the ethylene and propylene links in the copolymer: the content of propylene links decreases, while that of ethylene links increases (Figure 19). It is believed /52/ that this is due, in the first place, to the changes brought about in the organometallic complex catalyst as a result of its interaction with the diene compound.

Not only copolymers of ethylene with various α-olefins, but also copolymers of propylene with ethylene have been studied lately. The introduction of small amounts of ethylene into the polypropylene chain makes it possible to eliminate an important drawback of polypropylene — brittleness at low temperatures /145, 146/.

Other polyolefins, such as poly-4-methylpentene-1, can also be modified by copolymerization. Copolymerization of 4-methylpentene-1 with ethylene, propylene, butylene /100 — 104/, isobutylene /105/, butadiene /106, 107/ reduces the crystallinity of the material to differing extents, and enhances its solubility and elasticity. Copolymerizations of 4-methylpentene-1 with α-olefins which produce asymmetric side chains on the main chain — 3-methylpentene-1, 3-methylhexene-1, 4-methylhexene-1 /108/ and 4-methylpentene-2 /109/ also impair the crystalline structure.

COPOLYMERS OF ETHYLENE WITH POLAR MONOMERS

A very promising technique of modification of polyethylene so as to impart to it the desired properties is its copolymerization with various polar monomers: vinyl acetate and other vinyl esters, vinyl chloride, tetrafluoroethylene and other halogenated olefins, acrylic acid, methacrylic acid and their esters, etc.

The introduction of polar groups into macromolecules results in changed solubility of the polymer, and its melting point, elasticity, adhesive power and other characteristics. Some of the copolymers of ethylene with polar monomers serve as intermediate products in the modification processes involving the functional groups of the polar links; for example, copolymers of ethylene containing carboxyl groups are employed in the synthesis of ionomers.

Copolymers of ethylene with polar monomers are mainly prepared by free radical copolymerization. The reactions involved in such copolymerizations and their final products form the subject of extensive literature /110 — 112/.

The copolymerization is most often realized by a method similar to that employed in block polymerization of ethylene, under elevated (1,000 — 2,000 atm) pressures and temperatures (70 — 300°C) in the presence of oxygen or peroxy compounds as primers. Lower pressures (300 — 500 atm) may be applied if the copolymerization is realized in hydrocarbon solvents, in water or in emulsions.

The properties of ethylene copolymers depend on the structure and content of the comonomer and on the distribution of the comonomer links in the macromolecules /113/.

Variation of properties related to the link structure of the comonomer will depend, first and foremost, on its size and polarity. The introduction of polar groups into polyethylene chains results in intensified intramolecular and intermolecular effects. The copolymers are stiffer and their melting points increase; their dielectric properties obviously deteriorate and their power of adhesion to different materials increases.

If the side groups introduced into the polyethylene chain are about as big as a methylene group, no major changes occur in the crystallinity of the product. The only effect is changes in some of the lattice parameters. The physical properties vary in proportion to the number of the polar links which have been introduced (Figure 20). The melting point varies with the composition of the copolymers between the melting point of polyethylene and that of the polar homopolymer.

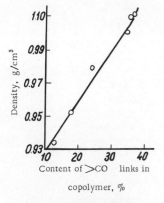

FIGURE 20. The density of the copolymers of ethylene with carbon monoxide as a function

of the content of $>$CO links

at 23°C /114/.

Copolymerization of ethylene with polar monomers having bulky substituent groups which do not fit into the crystal lattice of the polyethylene results in a decreased crystallinity. The parameters connected with the crystallinity change as well: the elasticity increases, and the hardness and the melting point decrease.

Of the two oppositely acting factors — polarity and dimensions of comonomer links — the latter becomes predominant if the comonomer links are large. Thus, for instance, ethylene copolymers with a small amount of vinyl acetate are more elastic than polyethylene and have a lower melting point. If the large acetate groups in the copolymer are converted to the much smaller hydroxyl groups by saponification, the product becomes stiffer and higher-melting than polyethylene. This is connected with the change in the steric factor, since the magnitudes of the dipole moments of the acetate and the hydroxyl groups are practically the same /113/.

The steric factor also affects the variation of the properties of copolymers as a function of their composition. If the links of the polar comonomer have small-sized substituents, which can be accommodated in the crystal lattice of the polyethylene, the properties of the copolymer gradually vary with the increase in the content of the polar links. The properties vary more rapidly with the composition if the polar monomer — say, vinyl acetate — has a large-sized substituent. Even if the content of such a comonomer is low, the crystallinity, stiffness and melting point of the copolymer are changed to a considerable extent (Figure 21).

An important factor which determines the properties of copolymers is the nature of the distribution of ethylene and comonomer links in the macro-molecule. It is known that the distribution is related to the product of the copolymerization rate constants. If this product is close to unity, the distribution is random, and becomes more ordered as the value of the product becomes smaller and there is a more regular alternation of both types of links in the chain. As an illustration, Figure 22 shows the effect of the differently ordered link distributions of the chain on the temperature function of dynamic losses of copolymers of ethylene with 20% vinyl acetate.

In the case of copolymers with a random distribution, the maximum loss occurs around −25°C, while in copolymers with a partly ordered distribution it occurs around +20°C. The reason for this difference is that the formation of ethylene blocks which are sufficiently large to crystallize is more likely in copolymers of an ordered structure (the minimum length of such a sequence, both in branched polyethylene and in ethylene-vinyl acetate copolymers is about 13 links /116/). Rearrangements of macromolecular chains in crystalline regions formed by ethylene blocks are possible at relatively high temperatures /21/.

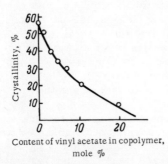

FIGURE 21. Crystallinity of ethylene-vinyl acetate copolymers as a function of their composition at 30°C /113, 115/.

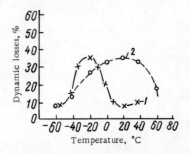

FIGURE 22. Temperature dependence of dynamic losses in ethylene-vinyl acetate copolymers for a random (1) and partly ordered (2) link distribution /21/.

Experimental determination of the distribution of the monomer units in the copolymer is quite a difficult task. Lyubetskii et al. /117, 118/ recently showed that the number of successive – CH_2-links in ethylene-vinyl acetate copolymers can be determined by IR absorption spectra. The determination was based on the relationship between the frequency of the rocking vibrations of methylene groups and the number of successive methylene groups (bounded by vinyl acetate links). Even at low contents of ethylene (25 mole %), there appear absorption bands at 743 and 725 cm^{-1}, which are absent in the spectra of poly (vinyl acetate), and the intensities of these bands increase with increasing ethylene content (Figure 23). If more than 50 mole % ethylene is present, an absorption band appears at 720 cm^{-1}. The bands at 743 and 725 cm^{-1} correspond to single links of ethylene carrying vinyl acetate links bound in the normal manner:

$$\cdots-CH_2-CH-CH_2-CH_2-CH_2-CH-\cdots$$

$$\begin{array}{ccc} & | & | \\ & O & O \\ & | & | \\ & C{=}O & C{=}O \\ & | & | \\ & CH_3 & CH_3 \end{array}$$

Normal
addition of
vinyl acetate

30

or in the anomalous manner:

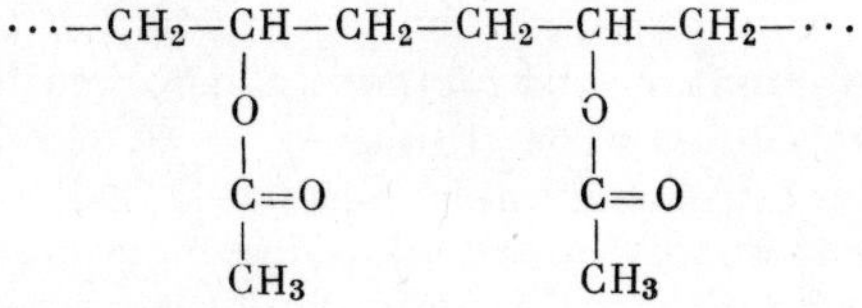

Anomalous addition
of vinyl acetate

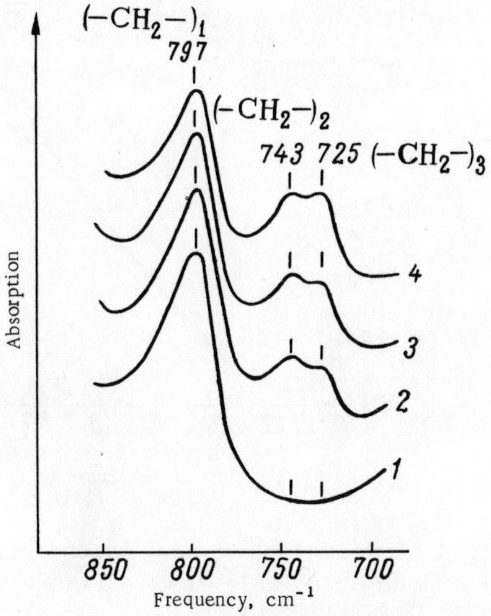

FIGURE 23. IR absorption spectra of poly(vinyl acetate) (1) and of copolymers of ethylene with vinyl acetate. Content of ethylene, mole %: 25 (2), 35 (3) and 43 (4) /117, 118/.

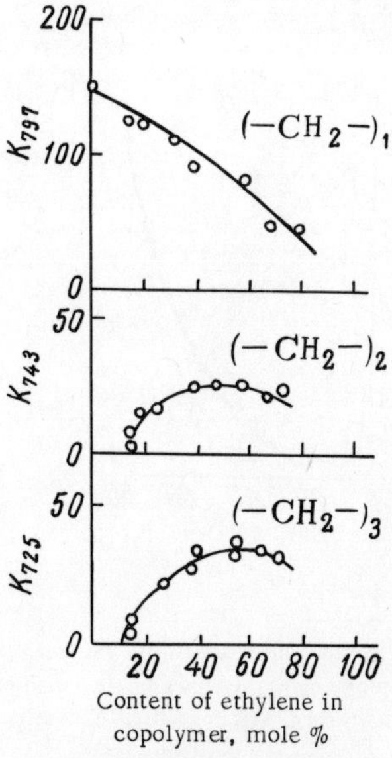

FIGURE 24. Variation of intensities of absorption bands at 725, 743 and 797 cm^{-1} with the composition of copolymers of ethylene with vinyl acetate /117, 118/.

Since the frequency of the band decreases with increasing number of successive methylene groups, the 725 cm^{-1} band was ascribed to the normal vinyl acetate bond $(-CH_2-)_3$, while the 743 cm^{-1} was related to the anomalous bond $(-CH_2-)_2$. The appearance of the 720 cm^{-1} band in the spectra of copolymers containing a large proportion of ethylene was related to $(-CH_2-)_n$ sequences in which $n > 5$. Unlike in /119/, the 797 cm^{-1} band was related to the rocking vibrations of single methylene links in poly (vinyl acetate) blocks. The intensities of the bands corresponding to one, two, three, five and more methylene groups in succession as a function of the composition of the copolymer are shown in Figures 24 and 25. Figure 25 shows that the number of ethylene blocks in the copolymer increases with increasing content of ethylene in the copolymer.

The authors /117, 118/ established the presence of "anomalously" bound vinyl acetate links and the proportion of such links, and used these results to deduce a general equation giving the composition of the copolymer in terms of the acts of formation and further transformations of the growing chains containing anomalously bound links.

Ethylene — vinyl acetate copolymers have been more thoroughly studied than any other ethylene copolymers with polar monomers. The copolymerization of ethylene with vinyl acetate can be realized in the bulk, in solution or in emulsion. Such copolymerizations may be initiated by organic peroxy compounds and azo compounds, by boron alkyls or by ionizing radiation.

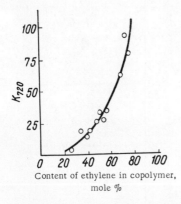

Content of ethylene in copolymer, mole %

FIGURE 25. Intensity of the 720 cm^{-1} band given by copolymers of ethylene with vinyl acetate as a function of their composition /117, 118/.

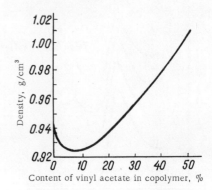

Content of vinyl acetate in copolymer, %

FIGURE 26. Density of copolymers of ethylene with vinyl acetate as a function of their composition at 25°C /120/.

Even a small proportion of vinyl acetate in an ethylene copolymer greatly reduces its crystallinity (Figure 21). This is evident, in particular, from the variation of the density of the copolymer with its composition (Figure 26). If the vinyl acetate content is low, the density decreases, attains a minimum and then increases to attain the value of 1.17 which is the density of poly (vinyl acetate). The melting point of the copolymer decreases with increasing content of vinyl acetate (Figure 27).

The curve giving the tensile strength of the copolymer as a function of its composition also has an optimum (Figure 28), past which the tensile strength rapidly decreases with increasing content of vinyl acetate. The elongation at break shows a marked increase with the increase in the content of vinyl acetate in the copolymer.

If the mutual proportion of the comonomers is varied, various products may be obtained, including both plastomers and elastomers. Copolymers of ethylene containing not more than 10 — 12 mole % vinyl acetate display properties close to those of high-pressure polyethylene, but are more elastic, more transparent and have a lower melting point /122/. Copolymers containing 13 — 25% vinyl acetate are rubberlike. If the content of vinyl acetate is 30 — 80%, the copolymers are soft and tacky at room temperature; if the proportion of vinyl acetate is further increased, the copolymerization products again become stiff and their properties begin to resemble those of poly(vinyl acetate). The solubilities of the copolymers in benzene, xylene and CCl_4 increase with the increasing content of vinyl acetate; if the content of vinyl acetate exceeds 40%, the copolymers become soluble in alcohol and acetone /121, 122/.

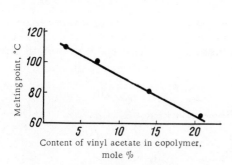

FIGURE 27. Melting points of copolymers of ethylene with vinyl acetate as a function of their composition /121/.

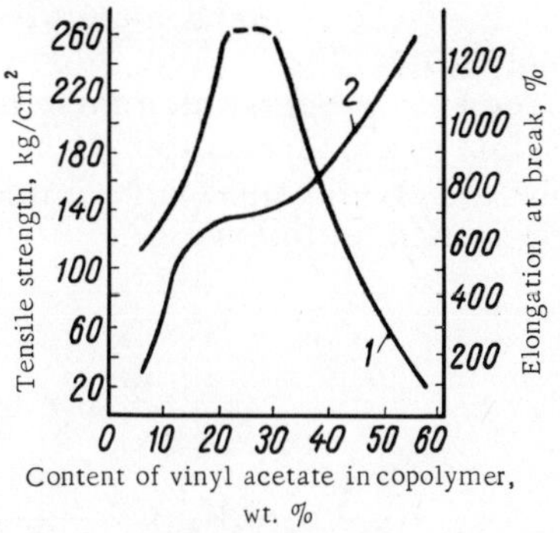

FIGURE 28. Tensile strength (1) and elongation at break (2) of ethylene-vinyl acetate copolymers as a function of their composition /120/.

    Copolymers of ethylene with vinyl acetate are readily cross-linked by peroxy compounds /120/, polycarboxylic acids /123, 124/ and ionizing radiation /121, 125/.

    Hydrolysis of copolymers of ethylene with vinyl acetate yields copolymers of ethylene with vinyl alcohol; partial hydrolysis yields ternary copolymers of ethylene, vinyl acetate and vinyl alcohol /126, 130/. The hydrolysis products have a high tensile strength and stiffness and, as distinct from poly(vinyl alcohol), are insoluble in water.

    Copolymerizations of ethylene with many vinyl esters other than vinyl acetate are also known.

    Of the copolymerization products of ethylene with acrylic monomers, copolymers of ethylene with ethyl acrylate are used in industry /131/ and have been studied in greatest detail /21, 132 — 134/. The products are strong, elastic, resistant to cracking and are transparent.

    Compounds which are incapable of homopolymerization, such as carbon monoxide, carbon dioxide and sulfur dioxide, can undergo free radical copolymerization with ethylene.

    Copolymers of ethylene with carbon monoxide are highly crystalline. The IR spectra of copolymers with 21% CO have an absorption band at 730 cm^{-1}, the intensity of which is related to crystallinity of the polyethylene type /135 — 138/. When the proportion of the CO links in the copolymer has increased to 43%, this band disappears /139/. The melting points of ethylene — carbon monoxide copolymers range between 90 and 200°C. The main drawback of these copolymers is that they are brittle. When heated above their melting temperature, they behave as thermo-reactive polymers, losing their fusibility and solubility. The process is accompanied by the liberation of water. It is considered /139/ that the copolymer acquires a tridimensional structure as a result of intermolecular reactions. Condensation of copolymers may be produced by alkalis /140, 141/.

The cross-linking of copolymers of ethylene with carbon monoxide by peroxy compounds, chloramine, and nitrous bases /114, 140, 142/ results in an increase in mechanical strength, softening temperature and a decrease in solubility.

The keto groups which form part of the macromolecular chain make it possible to perform different reactions in the chain, which yield various types of polymer products. Some of these reactions may be schematically represented as follows:

$$
\cdots -CH_2-CH_2-C-\cdots -
\begin{cases}
\xrightarrow{H_2} & \cdots -CH_2-CH_2-\overset{\displaystyle OH}{\underset{|}{CH}}-\cdots \quad (1) \\
\xrightarrow{HCN} & \cdots -CH_2-CH_2-\overset{\displaystyle OH}{\underset{|}{\underset{|}{C}}}-\cdots \quad (2) \\
& \qquad\qquad\qquad CN \\
\xrightarrow{NH_2OH} & \cdots -CH_2-CH_2-\underset{\|}{C}-\cdots \quad (3) \\
& \qquad\qquad\qquad NOH
\end{cases}
$$

where the left group carries $\underset{\|}{\overset{}{O}}$.

Hydrogenation of the copolymer of ethylene with carbon monoxide under pressure (scheme 1) in the presence of copper chromite as catalyst yields a polymer with hydroxyl groups /114/. Polycyanohydrin may be prepared by treating the copolymer with excess hydrocyanic acid in the presence of potassium cyanide (scheme 2), when up to 80% of the carbonyl groups are converted. Polyoximes are obtained when an aqueous solution of hydroxylamine is introduced into a solution of the copolymer in a hydrocarbon solvent (scheme 3); the degree of conversion of the hydroxyl groups is as high as 78%.

Copolymers of ethylene with sulfur dioxide have the formula:

$$
\cdots -CH_2-CH_2-\overset{\displaystyle O}{\underset{\displaystyle O}{\overset{\|}{\underset{\|}{S}}}}-\cdots
$$

They have a crystalline structure and their melting points are high. Copolymers with an equimolecular content of the comonomers melt above 300°C, and their melting point coincides with the decomposition point or else is higher. It would appear that the high melting point is produced by the strong intermolecular effects of the polar sulfone groups and by the regular structure of the copolymer /113/. The working of such copolymers below their decomposition point is rendered very difficult owing to their infusibility and their insolubility in all known solvents. Copolymers containing less than 50 mole % sulfur dioxide may be injection-molded and may be extruded at $180-220°C$ /143, 144/.

Bibliography

1. Boghetich, L. and G.W. Daues. — J. Polymer Sci., 61 (171): 3. 1962.
2. Smith, W.E., R.L. Stoffer, and R.B. Hannan. — J. Polymer Sci., 61 (171): 39. 1962.
3. Sirota, A.G., E.P. Ryabikov, A.L. Gol'denberg, P.A. Il'chenko, and L.F. Chopko. — Plast. Massy, No. 11: 5. 1965.
4. Gol'denberg, A.L., P.A. Il'chenko, A.G. Sirota, E.P. Ryabikov, and L.F. Kulikovskaya. — Plast. Massy, No. 6: 8. 1962.
5. Swan, P.R. — J. Polymer Sci., 56: 409. 1962.
6. Gol'denberg, A.L., V.M. Zapletnyak, and P.A. Il'chenko. — In: "Spektroskopiya polimerov," Kiev, Izdatel'stvo "Naukova Dumka." 1967.
7. Sopolimer etilena s propilenom nizkogo davleniya (Low-Pressure Copolymers of Ethylene and Propylene), p. 16, edited by S.V. Shchutskii. — Izdatel'stvo "Khimiya." 1965.
8. Gaylord, N.G. and H.F. Mark. Linear and Stereoregular Addition Polymers, New York, Interscience. 1959.
9. Reding, E.P. and E.R. Walter. — J. Polymer Sci., 38: 141. 1959.
10. Clark, A., J.P. Hogan, R.L. Banks, and W.G. Lanning. — Ind. Eng. Chem., 48 (7): 1152. 1956.
11. Smith, D.C. — Ind. Eng. Chem., 48 (7): 1162. 1956.
12. Buniyat-zade, A.A., K.G. Kasumov, and R.B. Sadykov. — Uchenye Zapiski Azerbaidzhanskogo Gosudarstvennogo Universiteta, 3: 90. 1959.
13. Dalin, M.A., A.A. Buniyat-zade, I.I. Pis'man, and A.A. Bakhshi-zade. — Azerbaidzhanskii Khim. Zhurnal, No. 4: 21. 1959.
14. Dalin, M.A., A.A. Bakhshi-zade, I.I. Pis'man, and A.A. Buniyat-zade. — Azerbaidzhanskii Khim. Zhurnal, No. 1: 25. 1960.
15. Dalin, M.A., I.I. Pis'man, A.A. Bakhshi-zade, and A.A. Buniyat-zade. — Doklady AN SSSR, 133 (5): 1084. 1960.
16. Dalin, M.A., R.I. Shenderova, I.I. Pis'man, A.A. Bakhshi-zade, L.Ya. Vedeneeva, and A.A. Buniyat-zade. — Azerbaidzhanskii Khim. Zhurnal, No. 1: 17. 1961.
17. Buniyat-zade, A.A. — Author's Summary of Thesis, Azerbaidzhanskii Gosudarstvennyi Universitet, Baku. 1961.
18. Dalin, M.A., I.I. Pis'man, A.A. Bakhshi-zade, A.A. Buniyat-zade, and S.D. Pokotilova. — Azerbaidzhanskii Khim. Zhurnal, No. 2: 9. 1961.
19. Pritchard, J.E., R.M. McClamery, and P.J. Boeke. — Brit. Plastics, No. 2: 58. 1960.

20. Polietilen srednego davleniya (Medium-Pressure Polyethylene), edited by S. V. Shchutskii. — Izdatel'stvo "Khimiya." 1965.

21. Takeshi, K. — Plastics Age (Osaka), 3(8): 34. 1965.

22. Hogan, J. P. Olefin Copolymerization with Supported Metal Oxide Catalyst. In: Copolymerization (edited by G. E. Ham), p. 89. — New York, Interscience. 1964.

23. Dalin, M. A., A. A. Buniyat-zade, and E. L. Bulatnikova. — Plast. Massy, No. 8:4. 1966.

24. Kambarov, Yu. G., N. M. Seidov, and A. A. Buniyat-zade. Poliolefiny (Polyolefins). — Baku, Azerb. Gos. Izdatel'stvo. 1966.

25. Belgian Patent 535082. 1955.

26. Indian Patent 53618. 1956.

27. US Patent 2825721. 1958.

28. US Patent 2692257. 1954.

29. GFR Patent 1001003. 1957.

30. British Patent 734501. 1955.

31. US Patent 2726231. 1955.

32. British Patent 748583. 1956.

33. Belgian Patent 545857. 1956.

34. British Patent 786014. 1957.

35. US Patent 2727024. 1955.

36. British Patent 783744. 1957.

37. US Patent 2728757. 1955.

38. US Patent 2691647. 1954.

39. British Patent 748634. 1956.

40. US Patent 2731452. 1956.

41. British Patent 753349. 1956.

42. Soviet Patent 175658. 1965; Byulleten' Izvbr. No. 20. 1965.

43. Lavrovskii, K. P., A. M. Brodskii, I. A. Musaev, and A. N. Rumyantsev. — Neftekhimiya, 2: 487. 1962.

44. ASTM, Standards on Plastics, Phil. Mag., 1049. 1958.

45. Egorov, N. M., Z. V. Arkhipova, I. N. Andreeva, A. L. Gol'denberg, V. M. Zapletnyak, and P. A. Il'chenko. — Plast. Massy, No. 1: 10. 1959.

46. Natta, G., G. Mazzanti, A. Valvassori, and G. Paiaro. — Chim. Ind., Milan, 39(9): 733. 1957.

47. Mazzanti, G., A. Valvassori, and G. Paiaro. — Chim. Ind., Milan, 39(9): 743. 1957.

48. Mazzanti, G., A. Valvassori, and G. Paiaro. — Chim. Ind., Milan, 39(10): 825. 1957.

49. Natta, G., A. Valvassori, G. Mazzanti, and G. Sartori. — Chim. Ind., Milan, 40(9): 717. 1958.

50. Natta, G., A. Valvassori, G. Mazzanti, and G. Sartori. — Chim. Ind., Milan, 40(11): 896. 1958.

51. Crespi, G., A. Valvassori, and G. Sartori. Ethylene Propylene Copolymers as Rubber. In: Copolymerization (edited by G. E. Ham), p. 231. — New York, Interscience. 1964.

52. Seidov, N. M. Novyi sinteticheskii kauchuk na osnove etilena i propilena (New Synthetic Rubber based on Ethylene and Propylene). — Baku, Azerbaidzhanskoe Gosudarstvennoe Izdatel'stvo. 1966.

53. British Patent 898261. 1962.
54. Hungarian Patent 149767. 1962.
55. Soviet Patent 172989. 1965; Byulleten' Izobretatelya, No. 14. 1965.
56. S e i d o v , N. M., M. A. D a l i n , Yu. G. K a m b a r o v , I. A. A r u t y u n o v , and A. A. B a k h s h i - z a d e . — Azerbaidzhanskii Khim. Zhurnal, No. 3:73. 1965.
57. S e i d o v , N. M., M. A. D a l i n , and A. I. A b a s o v . — Doklady AN SSSR, 166 (6): 1376. 1966.
58. S e i d o v , N. M. and A. I. A b a s o v . — Azerbaidzhanskii Khim. Zhurnal, No. 6: 54. 1965.
59. S e i d o v , N. M., I. A. A r u t y u n o v , M. A. D a l i n , and A. A. B a k h s h i - z a d e . — Neft' i Gaz, No. 7: 70. 1965.
60. S e i d o v , N. M., I. A. A r u t y u n o v , and M. A. D a l i n . — Neft' i Gaz, No. 10: 59. 1965.
61. S e i d o v , N. M., M. A. D a l i n , Yu. G. K a m b a r o v , I. A. A r u t y u n o v , and R. D. A b d u l l a e v . — Kauchuk i Rezina, No. 6: 3. 1966.
62. S e i d o v , N. M., I. A. A r u t y u n o v , and A. I. A b a s o v . — Uchenye Zapiski Azerbaidzhanskogo Gosudarstvennogo Universiteta, No. 3: 78. 1966.
63. B i e r , G., A. G u m b o l d t , and G. S c h l e i t z e r . — Makromol. Chem., 58: 43. 1962.
64. A m b e r g , L. O. and A. E. R o b i n s o n . — Rubber Plastics Age, 42 (7): 875. 1961.
65. N a t t a , G., G. M a z z a n t i , A. V a l v a s s o r i , and G. P a i a r o . — Chim. Ind., Milan, 41: 764. 1959.
66. British Patent 888986. 1962.
67. US Patent 2953592. 1960.
68. S e i d o v , N. M., M. A. D a l i n , and S. M. K y a z i m o v . — Doklady AN SSSR, 164 (4): 826. 1965.
69. S e i d o v , N. M., M. A. D a l i n , S. M. K y a z i m o v , R. M. A l i k u l i e v , and A. A. B a k h s h i - z a d e . — Azerbaidzhanskii Khim. Zhurnal, No. 3 : 46. 1966.
70. V a l v a s s o r i , A. and G. S a r t o r i . — Chim. Ind., Milan, 44: 1091. 1962.
71. V e r b a n c , J. J., M. S. F a w c e t t , and E. J. G o l d b e r g . — Ind. Eng. Chem. Prod. Res. Develop., 1: 70. 1962.
72. G l a d d i n g , E. K., B. S. F i s h e r , and J. W. C o l l e t t e . — Ind. Eng. Chem. Prod. Res. Develop., 1: 65. 1962.
73. French Patent 1386600. 1965.
74. French Patent 1370902. 1964.
75. S a r t o r i , G., A. V a l v a s s o r i , and S. V a i n a . — Atti Accad. Linc., 35 (6): 565. 1963.
76. Finnish Patent 32973. 1963.
77. French Patent 1389757. 1965.
78. French Patent 1392109. 1965.
79. British Patent 987734. 1965.
80. British Patent 997885. 1965.
81. US Patent 3208982. 1965.
82. French Patent 1353179. 1964,
83. Japanese Patent 22752. 1965.
84. French Patent 1362094. 1964.
85. French Patent 1375320. 1964.

86. French Patent 1370358. 1964.
87. GFR Patent 1163551. 1964.
88. French Patent 1371435. 1964.
89. French Patent 1375319. 1964.
90. French Patent 1377626. 1964.
91. French Patent 1430560. 1966.
92. French Patent 1386600. 1965.
93. French Patent 1397652. 1965.
94. French Patent 1413234. 1965.
95. French Patent 1416704. 1965.
96. French Patent 1424440. 1966.
97. French Patent 1428661. 1966.
98. Natta, G. and G. Crespi. — J. Polymer Sci., 61: 83. 1962.
99. French Patent 1345819. 1963.
100. British Patent 978101. 1964.
101. British Patent 982716. 1965.
102. French Patent 1380649. 1964.
103. French Patent 1389013. 1965.
104. French Patent 1410245. 1965.
105. British Patent 987316. 1965.
106. British Patent 982708. 1965.
107. French Patent 1381689. 1964.
108. British Patent 973827. 1964.
109. GFR Patent 1189274. 1965.
110. Raff, R. A. V. and J. B. Allison. Polyethylene, p. 114. — New
     York — London, Interscience. 1956.
111. Pieski, E. D. In: Polythene (edited by A. Renfrew and P. Morgan),
     p. 345. — New York, Interscience. 1960.
112. Mod. Plast. Encyclopedia Issue for 1962. — Plastics Catalogue Corp.
     pp. 256, 265, New York. 1961.
113. Terteryan, R. A., E. E. Braudo, and A. I. Dintses. — Uspekhi
     Khimii, 34(4): 666. 1965.
114. Brubaker, M. M., D. D. Coffman, and H. H. Hoehn. — J. Am.
     Chem. Soc., 74(6): 1509. 1952.
115. Nielsen, L. B. — J. Polymer Sci., 42: 357. 1960.
116. Kilian, H. G. — Kolloïd Z. and Z. fur Polymere, 189(1): 23. 1963.
117. Lyubetskii, S. G., B. L. Erusalimskii, and A. G.
     Gol'denberg. — Doklady AN SSSR, 172(6): 1372. 1967;
     Gol'denberg, A. L., L. I. Zyuzina, and S. G. Lyubetskii. —
     Vysoko-molekulyarnye Soedineniya, 139(7): 542. 1967.
118. Lyubetskii, S., B. Erusalimskii, and A. Gol'ddenberg. —
     Doklad na Mezhdunarodnom simpoziume po khimii vysokopoli-
     merov, Tokio. 1966.
119. Stokr, J. and B. Schneider. — Coll. Czech. Chem. Comm., 28,
     1946. 1963.
120. Bartl, H. and J. Peter. — Kautschuk Gummi, No. 2: 23. 1961.
121. Terteryan, R. A., A. I. Dintses, and M. V. Rysakov. —
     Zhurnal VKhO im. Mendeleeva, 8: 589. 1963.
122. Terteryan, R. A., A. I. Dintses, and M. V. Rysakov. —
     Neftekhimiya, 3: 719. 1963.

123. Belgian Patent 591575. 1960.
124. GFR Patent 1055232. 1959.
125. GFR Patent 1116394. 1966.
126. British Patent 634140. 1950.
127. US Patent 2386347. 1943.
128. US Patent 2399653. 1946.
129. British Patent 607911. 1948.
130. US Patent 2467774. 1949.
131. Mod. Plastics, 38(9): 41. 1961.
132. Bonotto, S. and B. H. Krevsky. — SPE J., 18: 555 1962.
133. Rubber Age, 91: 806. 1962.
134. Bonotto, S. and B. H. Krevsky. — Plastics World, 20(8): 32. 1962.
135. King, G. W., R. M. Hainen, and H. O. McMahon. — J. Appl. Phys., 20: 559. 1949.
136. Rugg, F. M., J. J. Smith, and L. H. Wartman. — J. Polymer Sci., 11: 1. 1953.
137. Stein, R. S. and G. B. B. M. Sutherland. — J. Chem. Phys., 21(2): 370. 1953.
138. Reding, F. P. and A. Brown. — J. Appl. Phys., 25: 848. 1954.
139. Braudo, E. E., A. A. Kadushin, and A. I. Dintses. — Neftekhimiya, 4(3): 441. 1963.
140. US Patent 2495286. 1950.
141. Curphy, E. G. — Can. Chem. Proc., 40(6): 78. 1956.
142. British Patent 597833. 1948.
143. US Patent 2943077. 1960.
144. US Patent 2976269. 1961.
145. Bier, G. — Angew. Chem., 73: 186. 1961.
146. Takagi, K. and S. Ioshioka. — Plastics Age (Osaka), 3(9): 11. 1965.

Chapter III

GRAFT AND BLOCK COPOLYMERS OF α-OLEFINS

GRAFT COPOLYMERS

The grafting of various monomers onto a polyolefin macromolecule is an attractive method by which polyolefins can be modified. This method has not yet been much employed in practice /1, 2/.

Depending on the chemical structure of the grafted links, it is possible to prepare graft copolymers with different properties: enhanced adhesive power and heat resistance, capacity to undergo ion exchange, etc.

The grafting may be realized in the bulk of the polymer which may be present as a suspension, or else in the surface layer of the finished article (fibers, films, etc.). Whatever the technique employed, active centers capable of initiating the propagation of the grafted chains must be produced in the polyolefin chain.

The two most important methods for the activation of poly-α-olefins are preliminary oxidation with formation of hydroperoxy groups and irradiation of the polymer. Polyolefin graft copolymers may also be prepared by chain transfer reactions and by photochemical initiation.

Preparation of graft polymers with preliminary oxidation of the polyolefin. Oxidation of polyolefins resulting in the formation of hydroperoxy groups, followed by thermal or other decomposition, yields free radicals which can be employed to initiate the propagation of grafted chains.

If the polyolefin contains tertiary carbon atoms, hydroperoxy groups in concentrations sufficient for subsequent grafting will be produced under relatively mild oxidation conditions. This applies, in the first instance, to polypropylene, the overall hydroperoxidation of which may be represented as follows:

$$\cdots-CH_2-CH-CH_2-CH-\cdots \xrightarrow{O_2} \cdots-CH_2-\underset{\underset{CH_3}{|}}{\overset{\overset{\displaystyle H}{\overset{|}{\underset{\displaystyle O}{\overset{|}{O}}}}}{C}}-CH_2-\underset{\underset{CH_3}{|}}{CH}-\cdots$$

The oxidizing agent may be atmospheric oxygen or ozone. Natta et al. /3/ subjected atactic polypropylene, dissolved in isopropylbenzene, to hydroperoxidation at 70°C. Methanol in the amount of 3 — 5% was added in order to suppress side reactions. Air was bubbled through the reaction mixture under atmospheric pressure. Under these conditions, the extent

40

of oxidation is quite large, but the macromolecule is not excessively degraded (Figure 29). The rate of formation of hydroperoxy groups may be accelerated by increasing the air pressure, by using ozone in lieu of air, or by adding a peroxide (e. g., benzoyl peroxide) to the solution (Figure 30).

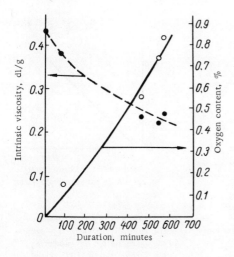

FIGURE 29. Hydroperoxidation of atactic poly-propylene, dissolved in isopropylbenzene (concentration 15.5%, methanol content 4%, 70°C /3/.

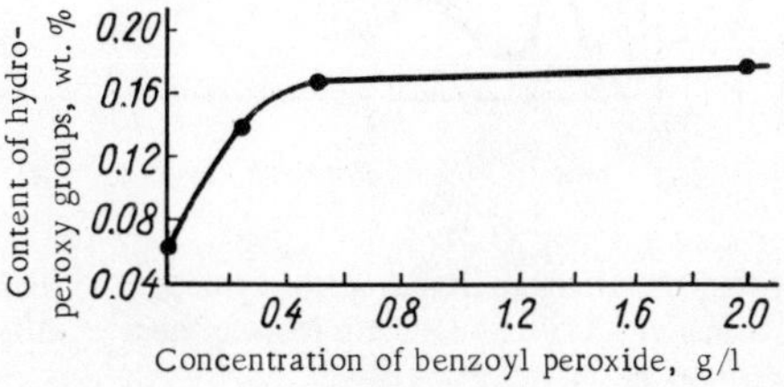

FIGURE 30. Rate of hydroperoxidation of a copolymer of ethylene with 6.5 mole % propylene as a function of the concentration of benzoyl peroxide (20 g/l toluene, 4% methanol, 75°C, air pressure 10 atm, duration 1 hour).

Heterogeneous hydroperoxidation of polypropylene takes place mostly in the amorphous regions and on the outer surfaces of crystalline regions /3/.

The content of hydroperoxy groups as a function of the duration of the oxidation was studied /4/ for the case of atactic polypropylene. It was found that the hydroperoxy group content passes a maximum and then decreases owing to decomposition (Figure 31) /4, 5/. The activation energy of formation of hydroperoxy groups is 24 − 25 kcal/mole, while their decomposition energy is 27 kcal/mole /4, 6/.

45

The decomposition of hydroperoxy groups is a bimolecular reaction which essentially involves the interaction between a hydroperoxy group and a hydrogen atom, the latter being mostly attached to a tertiary carbon atom in the macromolecular chain /7/:

$$ROOH + RH \longrightarrow R\dot{O} + \dot{R} + H_2O$$

Both types of macroradicals formed − $R\dot{O}$ and $\dot{R}$ − are capable of initiating the growth of grafted chains. A study of the grafting of methyl methacrylate onto oxidized polypropylene showed /8/ that about one-half of the grafted chains are bound to the main chain via an oxygen bridge, while the other chains are bound to the main chain by a C−C bond. This was established by splitting off the methyl methacrylate chains bound via an oxygen atom by hydrogen iodide and determining the loss in weight.

The grafting may be realized in the bulk, in solution or in the gas phase. The main parameters which determine the rate of grafting are the degree of preliminary oxidation of the polyolefin, temperature, monomer concentration and the duration of the process.

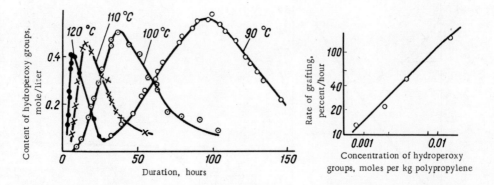

FIGURE 31. Content of hydroperoxy groups as a function of the duration of oxidation of atactic polypropylene at different temperatures /4, 5/.

FIGURE 32. Rate of grafting of acrylonitrile onto polypropylene as a function of the concentration of hydroperoxy groups. Temperature 110°C, vapor pressure of acrylonitrile 2.34 atm /9/

It was found /9/ in the course of a study of the grafting of acrylonitrite onto a polypropylene fiber that the grafting rate is directly proportional to the concentration of the hydroperoxy groups (Figure 32). The difference between this reaction rate and the reaction order of 0.5 with respect to the primer, which is usually observed in free radical polymerization, is most likely due to the low probability of bimolecular termination of the grafted chains, owing to the limited mobility of macroradicals under conditions of a heterogeneous process /10/.

As the temperature increases, so does the decomposition rate of the hydroperoxy groups and thus also the rate of the grafting reaction (Figure 33) /11/. The temperature may affect not merely the grafting rate, but also the structure of the resulting product. The grafting usually takes place in the amorphous fraction, and the grafted chains do not penetrate to any significant depth into the crystalline regions /12/. However, at temperatures high enough to enhance the mobility of the elements of the crystalline structure, grafting can take place in crystalline regions as well. The graft copolymers prepared under these conditions differ from one another in the type of their crystalline formations. This may be illustrated /11/ by considering the products of grafting acrylamide onto the copolymer of ethylene with 7 mole % propylene /11/. The product of grafting effected in a heterogeneous system at 130°C, i.e., above the melting range of the initial copolymer (116 − 120°C), was less highly ordered than the product obtained by grafting at a lower temperature (100°C).

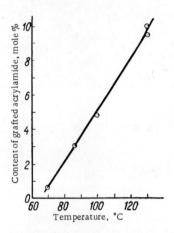

FIGURE 33. Content of acrylamide grafted onto ethylene — propylene copolymer as a function of the temperature (duration of reaction 3 hours, content of propylene in initial copolymer 7 mole %, concentration of hydroperoxy groups 0.1 wt.%) /11/.

A comparison of X-ray diffraction curves given by products of graftings effected at various temperatures shows that as the grafting temperature increases, the crystallinity of the graft copolymers decreases (Figure 34).

The hydroperoxides may decompose not only by a bimolecular, but also by a monomolecular mechanism:

$$ROOH \longrightarrow R\dot{O} + \dot{O}H$$

The resulting free radicals $\dot{O}H$, together with polymeric free radicals, are capable of initiating the polymerization of the monomer, in the presence of which the hydroperoxy groups are decomposed. The polymerization initiated by OH radicals leads to the formation of the homopolymer. The same result is obtained if the polymerization takes place on active centers formed by chain transfer onto the monomer or the solvent. The homopolymerization initiated by hydroxyl radicals is largely suppressed by working in redox systems, since under these conditions the polymerization is initiated by macroradicals only:

$$\cdots-CH_2-CH-CH_2-\cdots \xrightarrow{Fe^{2+}} \cdots-CH_2-CH-CH_2-\cdots + OH^- + Fe^{3+}$$
$$\qquad\qquad | \qquad\qquad\qquad\qquad\qquad\qquad |$$
$$\qquad\qquad OOH \qquad\qquad\qquad\qquad\qquad O$$
$$\qquad\qquad\qquad\qquad\qquad\qquad\qquad\qquad\qquad \cdot$$

$$\cdots-CH_2-CH-CH_2-\cdots \xrightarrow{M} \cdots-CH_2-CH-CH_2-\cdots$$

Thus, for instance, the formation of the homopolymer was successfully prevented during the grafting of polyacrylic acid onto polypropylene in the presence of ferrous sulfate /13/. Grafting of monomers from the gas phase /14 — 16; 10, p. 244/ is a very promising method of suppression of homopolymerization on active centers formed by chain transfer onto the monomer or the solvent, since the rate of such chain transfer is very slow under these experimental conditions.

The reaction of chain transfer, in particular chain transfer onto the polymer, can be used to prepare graft copolymers even without a preliminary oxidation. If any monomer is polymerized in the presence of a free-radical primer and a polyolefin (e. g., polypropylene), macroradicals will

43

be formed as a result of chain transfer onto the polymer:

$$\cdots-CH_2-\overset{\bullet}{C}H+\cdots-CH-CH_2-\cdots\ \longrightarrow\ \cdots-CH_2-CH_2+\cdots-\overset{\bullet}{C}-CH_2-\cdots$$
$$\underset{X}{|}\qquad\underset{CH_3}{|}\qquad\qquad\qquad\underset{X}{|}\qquad\underset{CH_3}{|}$$

The grafting takes place owing to the initiation of the polymerization by the macroradical:

$$\cdots-CH_2-\overset{\bullet}{\underset{\underset{CH_3}{|}}{C}}-\cdots+CH_2{=}\overset{\underset{\underset{X}{|}}{}}{CH}\ \longrightarrow\ \cdots-CH_2-\overset{\overset{X-\overset{\bullet}{C}H}{|}\;\overset{CH_2}{|}}{\underset{\underset{CH_3}{|}}{C}}-\cdots$$

The product will clearly consist of a mixture of the graft copolymer and the homopolymer. Poly(vinyl acetate), poly(vinyl chloride), polystyrene and polyvinylformamide have all been grafted onto polyethylene by this method /17/.

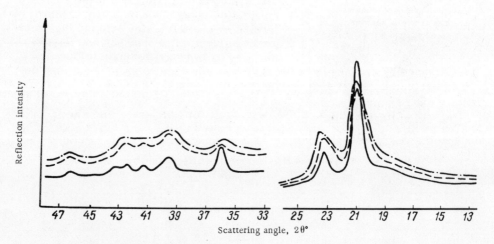

FIGURE 34. X-ray diffraction curves /11/:

―――― – initial copolymer of ethylene with 7 mole % propylene;   ----- – product containing 3.15 mole % grafted acrylamide, reaction temperature 100°C; —·—·– the same at 130°C.

Preparation of graft copolymers with the aid of ionizing radiation. Polymers can be activated by irradiation with a view to subsequent grafting. Electron accelerators and Co[60] radiation are the most commonly used sources of radiation.

The nature of the active centers which participate in graft polymerization depends on the conditions of irradiation of the polymer. The effect of radiation on the polymer in vacuo or in an inert gas medium consists in the rupture of covalent bonds (say, C—H bonds) and in the formation of free radicals:

$$\cdots-CH_2-CH_2-CH_2-\cdots \longrightarrow \cdots-CH_2-\overset{\bullet}{C}H-CH_2-\cdots+H$$

Some of the free radicals recombine with formation of cross-links between the chains:

$$
\begin{array}{c}
\cdots-CH_2-CH-CH_2-\cdots \\
\overset{\bullet}{+} \\
\cdots-CH_2-\overset{\bullet}{C}H-CH_2-\cdots
\end{array}
\quad\longrightarrow\quad
\begin{array}{c}
\cdots-CH_2-CH-CH_2-\cdots \\
\vert \\
\cdots-CH_2-\overset{}{C}H-CH_2-\cdots
\end{array}
$$

The remainder — the so-called "captured" free radicals — are preserved for a certain period of time, the duration of which depends on the conditions of irradiation, on the conditions under which the polymer is stored and on the structure of the polymer. If the temperature is decreased, the lifetime of the free radicals will become longer. Deep freezing will prolong the lifetime of "captured" radicals to several days, even if the irradiated polymer is exposed to the atmosphere.

The free radical concentration largely depends on the degree of crystallinity of the polyolefin. The probable reason for this is the fact that captured free radicals are mostly found in crystalline regions. The probability of recombination is smaller in crystalline than in amorphous regions, since the macrochains forming part of crystalline regions are less mobile. Figure 35 shows the intensity of the EPR signal, which is a measure of the free radical concentration in ethylene copolymers, as a function of the aging time in the air at various temperatures following irradiation by accelerated electrons in an inert medium. More highly crystalline copolymers have higher free radical concentrations immediately after irradiation and on subsequent exposure to the air.

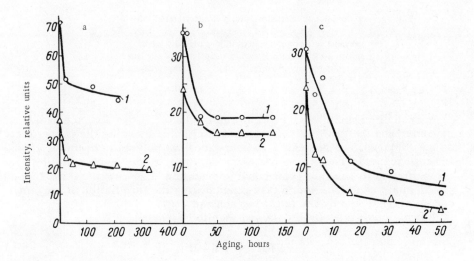

FIGURE 35. EPR signal intensity given by ethylene copolymers as a function of the aging time in the air at 25°C (a), 45°C (b) and 70°C (c) after irradiation with accelerated electrons, 2.2 MeV, 70 Mrad, in nitrogen /18/:

1 — copolymer of ethylene with propylene, crystallinity 75%, 2.2 methyl groups per 100 carbon atoms;
2 — copolymer of ethylene with α-butylene, crystallinity 66%, 2.5 methyl groups per 100 carbon atoms.

That the captured free macroradicals are mainly concentrated in crystalline regions is also confirmed by the IR spectra of ethylene co-polymers with varying degrees of crystallinity which have been irradiated and then exposed to the atmosphere at room temperature /18/. The intensity of the absorption band at 1,710 cm^{-1}, which is given by carbonyl groups formed by the reaction between oxygen and the captured free radicals, is stronger in the case of more crystalline products (Figure 36). The free macroradicals may act as active centers bringing about graft polymerization directly during irradiation in the monomer medium.

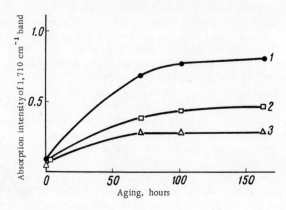

FIGURE 36. Intensity of the 1,710 cm^{-1} band given by co-polymers of ethylene as a function of the aging time
in the air at room temperature after irradiation with accelerated electrons, 2.2 MeV, 70 Mrad, in nitrogen /18/:

1 — copolymer of ethylene with propylene, crystallinity 75%, 2.2 methyl groups per 100 carbon atoms; 2 — copolymer of ethylene with propylene, crystallinity 69%, 3.6 methyl groups per 100 carbon atoms; 3 — copolymer of ethylene with α-butylene, crystallinity 61%, 2.5 methyl groups per 100 carbon atoms.

In another variant, the irradiation is conducted in the absence of the monomer and the graft polymerization is effected by using the post-effect on the captured free radicals. In both cases the polyolefin becomes cross-linked, but the degree of cross-linking is small, since small radiation doses are sufficient to activate graft copolymerization.

The main reactions which take place during the irradiation of polyethylene can be represented by the following scheme /19/.

Formation of macroradicals and atomic hydrogen:

$$RH \xrightarrow[Y]{K_1} \dot{R} + \dot{H}$$

Formation of macroradicals and molecular hydrogen:

$$RH + \dot{H} \xrightarrow{K_2} \dot{R} + H_2$$

Formation of vinylene groups:

$$\dot{R} + \dot{R} \xrightarrow{K_3} R_= + RH$$

Reaction between vinylene groups and macroradicals:

$$R_= + \dot{R} \xrightarrow{K_4} R\dot{R}$$

Formation of cross-links:

$$R\dot{R} + RH \xrightarrow{K_5} RRH + \dot{R}$$

In these equations Y is a factor depending on the irradiation intensity and on the nature of the primary act and $R_=$ is a macromolecule with vinylene groups.
  In a quasistationary state

$$\frac{d\,[\dot{R}]}{dt} = \frac{d\,[\dot{H}]}{dt} = \frac{d\,[R\dot{R}]}{dt} = 0$$

$$\frac{d\,[\dot{R}]}{dt} = K_1[RH]Y + K_2[RH]\,[\dot{H}] - 2K_3\,[\dot{R}]^2 - K_4\,[R_=]\,[\dot{R}] +$$

$$+ K_5\,[R\dot{R}]\,[RH] = 0$$

$$\frac{d\,[\dot{H}]}{dt} = K_1\,[RH]\,Y - R_2\,[RH]\,[\dot{H}] = 0$$

$$\frac{d\,[R\dot{R}]}{dt} = K_4\,[R_=]\,[\dot{R}] - K_5\,[R\dot{R}]\,[RH] = 0$$

Hence

$$[\dot{R}] = \left(\frac{K_1\,[RH]\,Y}{K_3} \right)^{1/2}$$

This kinetic scheme is only a very much simplified representation of the true process. In particular, it is assumed that the reaction which results in the formation of vinylene groups,

$$\cdots{-}CH_2{-}CH{-}CH_2{-}\cdots \qquad \cdots{-}CH_2{-}CH_2{-}CH_2{-}\cdots$$
$$\overset{+}{\underset{\cdots{-}CH_2{-}\dot{C}H{-}CH_2{-}\cdots}{}} \longrightarrow \overset{+}{\cdots{-}CH_2{-}\dot{C}H{=}CH{-}CH_2{-}\cdots}$$

is strictly bimolecular.
  It would be justifiable to assume that the probability of such reactions between the migrating free radicals is higher in the amorphous than in the crystalline regions, owing to their higher mobility in the former than in the latter phase. In fact, however, the content of vinylene groups is independent of the crystallinity of the polyolefin and depends only on the radiation dose absorbed. This may be seen in Figure 37, which represents the intensity of the absorption band at 965 cm^{-1}, given by the trans-vinylene group, as a

function of the dose absorbed by polyolefins having different crystallinities. This fact, in conjunction with the finding of Lowton et al. /20/ to the effect that the content of trans-vinylene groups is independent of the physical condition of polyethylene between −150 and +150°C, makes it legitimate to conclude that the mechanism of formation of trans-vinylene groups is essentially unconnected with effects which take place between the chains. It would appear that trans-vinylene groups are formed in those sites in the macromolecule which have two contiguous carbon atoms with one lone electron on each atom:

$$\cdots-CH_2-\overset{\bullet}{C}H-\overset{\bullet}{C}H-CH_2-\cdots \longrightarrow -\cdots CH_2-CH=CH-CH_2-\cdots$$

The free-radicals formed by two contiguous carbon atoms may be the result of migration of two free radicals along the macromolecular chain or else, which is less likely, of the rupture of two contiguous C−H bonds as a result of irradiation.

The following equation /21/ describes the relationship between the concentration of the macroradicals and the radiation dose and the duration of the irradiation:

$$[\overset{\bullet}{R}] = K_1 I \tau \left(1 - e^{-t/\tau}\right)$$

where K_1 is the rate constant of macroradical formation, I is the radiation dose, τ is the lifetime of free radicals and t is the duration of the irradiation.

If the irradiation is prolonged, this equation is simplified as follows:

$$[\overset{\bullet}{R}]_{t\to\infty} = K_1 I \tau$$

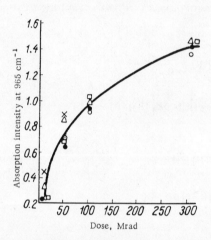

FIGURE 37. Intensity of the 965 cm^{-1} band as a function of the absorbed dose of accelerated electrons (2 MeV) /18/:

□ − low-pressure polyethylene, 83% crystalline; ○ − low-pressure polyethylene, 78% crystalline; △ − ethylene-propylene copolymer, 75% crystalline; × − ethylene-propylene copolymer, 69% crystalline; ● − ethylene−α-butylene copolymer, 61% crystalline.

If graft polymerization is considered to be an ordinary chain polymerization and its special features due to the heterogeneous nature of the process are ignored /10, p. 235/, a kinetic expression similar to that for a free radical polymerization is obtained:

$$v = K_2 \left(\frac{K_1}{K_3}\right)^{1/2} [M] [\overset{\bullet}{R}]^{1/2}$$

where K_1 is the initiation rate constant, K_2 is the constant of the growth rate of the grafted chains, K_3 is the rate constant of chain termination, [M] is the monomer concentration and [R] is the macroradical concentration.

Grafting based on the utilization of the post-effect, initiated by captured radicals, is to be preferred to grafting involving simultaneous irradiation of polymer and monomer, since in the former case homopolymerization is practically absent. However, homopolymerization can also be prevented in the latter case if the polyolefin is irradiated in the presence of monomer vapor /14—16/. The radiation-initiated graft polymerization from the gas phase onto polyethylene and polypropylene has been described for a number of monomers, including acrylonitrile, acrylic acid, vinyl acetate, styrene, methyl methacrylate, etc.

It has been experimentally shown that the main factors which determine the extent of grafting from the gas phase initiated by captured radicals are the radiation dose, the surface area of the polymeric material, the duration of the contact with the monomer, the vapor pressure of the monomer, and the temperature of contact between the vapors and the irradiated polymer /22/. The rate of graft polymerization initiated by macroradicals is proportional to the square root of the radiation dose. This has been demonstrated in the case of styrene grafted onto polypropylene fiber /21/. This relationship between the rate of graft polymerization and the radiation dose, and the reaction order of 0.5 with respect to the primer for ordinary reactions of free radical polymerization, both indicate that the growing graft chains are terminated by a bimolecular mechanism.

If the polymer is irradiated together with the monomer, the grafting rate may be intensified by diluting the monomer with a solvent. Thus, when styrene or methyl acrylate are diluted with methanol, the grafting rates onto polyethylene and polypropylene are much accelerated (Table 9) /23, 24/.

TABLE 9. Rate of graft polymerization as a function of the dilution of the monomer with methanol /24/

Polyolefin	Monomer	Monomer content, vol. %	Dose rate, Mrad/hour	Extent of grafting, percent/Mrad
High-pressure polyethylene	Styrene	100	0.070	61
		50	0.070	117
Low-pressure polyethylene	Styrene	100	0.081	127
		50	0.081	414
	Methyl acrylate	100	0.061	82
		30	0.061	124
Polypropylene	Styrene	100	0.080	84
		50	0.080	319
	Methyl acrylate	100	0.021	119
		50	0.021	134

The enhanced rate of grafting displayed by diluted monomers is due to two factors. One of them is connected with the gel effect caused by the decreased solubility of the grafted chains in the monomer-monomer system; the other is the increase in the rate of diffusion of the monomer into the polymer /23/.

Oda and Hoshino /25/ demonstrated that it was possible to accelerate the rate of grafting from the gas phase by diluting the monomer vapors with an inert gas. They studied the gas phase graft copolymerization on low-density polyethylene, which had been previously γ-irradiated in the air. At a low pressure of styrene vapor, when the reaction rate varies with the pressure and is determined by the diffusion of monomer vapor into the polymer, dilution of styrene vapor with argon reduced the reaction rate. However, at higher pressures of styrene vapor, when the reaction rate varied more strongly with temperature than with pressure, the addition of argon to monomer vapors resulted in an acceleration of the process. The addition of argon reduced the concentration of the monomer in polyethylene; accordingly, the increase in the reaction rate could only be explained by the gel effect, since the grafting took place in a very viscous medium.

An increase in the temperature at which graft copolymerization takes place may result in a reduction of the reaction rate. Such effect, which was noted /26/ during the grafting of styrene onto polyethylene films between 0° and 53°C, was probably due to the increased rate of recombination of the captured radicals at elevated temperatures. The effect of the temperature on the grafting rate will depend on the crystallinity of the polyolefin. The rate of grafting onto highly crystalline polyethylenes markedly increases with the temperature, while the grafting rate onto more amorphous polyethylenes is practically independent of the temperature. This is because most of the captured radicals are located in crystalline regions, into which the monomer diffuses faster, the closer is the temperature to the melting point of crystalline regions.

Irradiation of polyolefins in the air also results in their activation with a view to subsequent grafting. Ionizing radiation acting on the polymer in the presence of atmospheric oxygen results in the formation of peroxide and hydroperoxide groups. At room temperature these groups are stable, while at elevated temperatures they decompose with formation of macroradicals, capable of initiating graft polymerization. Acrylonitrile, methyl methacrylate, N-vinylcarbazole have been grafted onto polyethylene, and acrylonitrile has been grafted onto polypropylene in this manner /26 — 31/.

It was shown by Bakh /32/ for the case of low homologs of polyethylene (n-heptane and isooctane) that the concentration of the peroxy and hydroperoxy groups is proportional to the radiation dose absorbed. However, the grafting rate is not proportional to the square root of the dose, as could have been expected for a bimolecular chain termination mechanism. It was found by studying the kinetics of grafting of acrylonitrile onto polyethylene /28/ and of acrylic acid onto polypropylene /33/ that the reaction rate is proportional to the radiation dose. This is due /28/ to the fact that the grafting reaction is heterogeneous, so that the bimolecular termination of the growing grafted chains is retarded by their low mobility in the bulk of the polymer. The rates of formation of active centers and of chain growth are not affected by the heterogeneous nature of the process, but the degree of grafting increases with an increasing dose of preliminary irradiation (up to a certain limit).

Chen and Friedlander /34/ made a comparative study of graft polymerization of styrene onto a polyethylene film initiated by benzoyl peroxide and initiated by radiation. The grafting was effected by three methods: by γ-irradiation of the film immersed in the liquid monomer at room temperature; by β-irradiation of the film in the air, with subsequent immersion into the monomer at 65°C; and by treating the film at 65°C with liquid monomer containing benzoyl peroxide. The grafting was most advanced when the film had been subjected to preliminary irradiation in the air; it was least when benzoyl peroxide had been employed.

Photochemical synthesis of graft copolymers. The initiation of graft copolymerization may be effected by exposing the polymer-monomer system to UV light in the presence of a photosensitizer. The sensitizer absorbs the radiation energy and becomes decomposed into free radicals which accept hydrogen atoms from the macromolecular chain of the polyolefin. The macroradicals formed as a result are capable of initiating the polymerization of the monomer present in the system.

Free radicals formed by photolysis of the sensitizer also initiate homopolymerization. Formation of homopolymers can be almost totally prevented if the irradiation is effected on the polymer already containing the sensitizer, after which the polymer is brought into contact with the monomer and the grafting is realized by utilizing the post-effect.

Acrylamide has been photochemically grafted onto polyethylene films, using benzophenone as sensitizer /35, 36/.

Iwakura and Takeda /37/ studied the grafting of vinyl monomers onto polypropylene, using the photoinitiating system benzophenone — salt of a bivalent metal of variable valency. The addition of copper acetate or cobalt acetate increases the yield of the graft polymer, probably owing to the oxidation of the semiquinone benzophenone radical to benzophenone in the presence of the salt.

Structure and properties of graft copolymers. The structural ordering, which is typical of a given polyolefin, is retained even after intensive grafting, since the grafting reaction mainly takes place in the amorphous regions and on the surface of crystalline regions. As a result of the grafting, the copolymers become inhomogeneous; moreover, the course of a given graft polymerization will depend on the microstructure of the polymer. Geleji and Odor /38/, who studied the grafting of methyl methacrylate onto polypropylene fibers and films which had previously been γ-irradiated in the atmosphere, concluded that the microstructure of the polymer affects the processes of recombination, the lifetime of the free radicals and the formation of peroxy and hydroperoxy groups.

The microstructure determines the rate of recombination of free radicals with hydrogen atoms, since the diffusion rate of hydrogen in the material increases with increasing distance between the macromolecules. The crystal structure of the polymer interferes with the diffusion of the monomer and favors the stabilization of the free radicals until they can react with the medium. The formation of peroxy and hydroperoxy groups is also connected with the microstructure, since it is determined by the diffusion of oxygen towards the free radicals, the more amorphous polymers containing more oxygen than the highly crystalline polymers. This is the explanation given by the authors for the fact that the rate and the extent of grafting are lower in oriented than in nonoriented fibers.

A study /14/ of the product of gas phase grafting of acrylonitrile onto polyethylene fiber showed that the grafted polymer is oriented.

That graft copolymers are heterogeneous and that the supermolecular structure of the initial polymer affects the course of graft copolymerization is also indicated by the results of studies of grafting styrene, methyl methacrylate and vinyl chloride onto isotactic polypropylene /3/, and styrene, vinyl acetate and acrylic acid onto polyethylene /39 — 41/. Graft copolymers of this kind are mixtures of the crystalline polymer with the graft copolymer proper, the latter being the product of grafting onto the

56

surface of supermolecular structures /12/. This structure of graft
copolymers of polyolefins is also reflected in their properties. When
graft copolymers are heated, the crystalline regions melt at temperatures
corresponding to the point of fusion of the base polymer. However, the
resistance to heat and the mechanical properties at elevated temperatures
can be improved by grafting polar monomers such as acrylonitrile,
vinylidene chloride /42/ or acrylamide /11/.

Grafting may considerably improve the adhesion of polyolefins to
different materials. An ethylene-propylene copolymer containing about
4 mole % acrylamide adheres to aluminum foil five times more strongly than
the initial copolymer /11/. The uptake of printing dyes by polyethylene
may be improved by surface-grafting of, say, vinylpyrrolidone. The
affinity of polyolefins to dyes is enhanced by the introduction of functional
groups capable of reacting with acid or basic dyes; this is achieved by
surface graft copolymerization with acrylic and methacrylic acids, acrylonitrile, acrylamide, vinylpyridine and other monomers. The degree of
grafting need only be $4-8$ wt. % to ensure adequate improvement of
dyeability, without impairing the mechanical properties of the polymer
/10, p. 257/.

Copolymers in which styrene has been grafted onto polyolefins (polyethylene, ethylene-propylene copolymers) can be sulfonated or aminated
in the grafted chains, after which they behave as ion exchangers /43−46/.
The exchange capacity of such anion and cation exchangers is about
4 meq/g. Ion exchange membranes prepared by grafting styrene onto a
polyethylene film and phosphorylating, have capacities of up to 5.5 meq/g /45/.

The specific properties which appear in polyolefins as the result of grafting include a reduced permeability to gases and vapors. Grafting small
amounts of styrene or acrylonitrile onto a film of polyethylene is accompanied by an increased packing density in the amorphous regions, with a
corresponding decrease in the permeability of the film. If the extent of
grafting is larger, the permeability increases, probably because the product
becomes more amorphous /1/.

BLOCK COPOLYMERS

Block copolymers of different types are prepared by polymerization of
α-olefins or by modification of polymeric products.

Block copolymers of α-olefins may be prepared /47−51/ by using
catalyst systems which preserve their activity for a long time. In so doing,
advantage is taken of the long lifetime of the growing chains, which may
be several hours. Such catalyst systems include $TiCl_4 + LiAlR_2$ and
$VOCl_3 + AlR_2Cl$ /50/. Block copolymers are prepared as follows: ethylene,
for example, is polymerized first to a homopolymeric block, the residual
ethylene is expelled, and the second monomer — say, propylene or α-butylene
— or a mixture of monomers is added. If these operations are continued,
it is possible to prepare macromolecular chains consisting of alternating
different homopolymer blocks or of homopolymer and copolymer blocks.
Chains of copolymer blocks of different compositions can also be prepared.
The identity of the final product of such successive polymerizations largely

depends on the lifetimes of the growing macromolecular chains. If the lifetime is sufficiently long, block copolymers are obtained; if short, a mixture of homopolymers is obtained; in an intermediate case, the product will be a mixture of the block copolymer with the homopolymers /52/.

The properties of the products of block copolymerization are determined by the composition, length and microstructure of individual blocks.

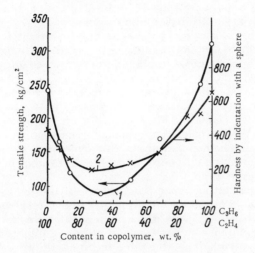

FIGURE 38. Tensile strength (1) and hardness (2) of block copolymers of ethylene with propylene as a function of their composition /51/.

TABLE 10. Properties of block copolymers of propylene with ethylene, homopolymers and mixture of polypropylene with polyethylene /51/

Polymer	Content of soluble fraction, %	Relative viscosity	Hardness, by indentation with a sphere	Impact strength			Crystallization temperature, °C
				20°C	0°C	-20°C	
Polyethylene	1	3.5	440	9	8	6.5	127—131
Polypropylene	4	6.9	730	7	2.3	1.9	160—165
Product of random co-polymerization of 90 wt. pts. propylene with 10 wt. pts. ethylene. .	30.4	6.4	375	23.0	4.6	2.0	150—159
Mixture of 90 wt. pts. polypropylene with 10 wt. pts. polyethylene . .	4	6.4	708	7.3	2.8	1.9	157—163
Block copolymers, 90 wt. pts. propylene links with 10 wt. pts. ethylene links	4.2—9.6	5.4—6.8	379—708	16.4—35.2	3.9—24.4	2.3—4.1	155—164

Table 10 contains comparative data on the properties of linear polyethylene and polypropylene, of a random copolymer and block copolymer of propylene with ethylene and of a mixture of polyethylene with polypropylene.

Block copolymers of ethylene and propylene are not as hard and not as strong as the linear homopolymers (Figure 38), but have a higher impact strength. The hardness and the tensile strength of block copolymers are higher than those of high-pressure polyethylene /51/. The changed properties of block copolymers are explained by the decrease in crystallinity as compared to the crystallinity of homopolymers.

Highly crystalline block copolymers, in particular the so-called polyallomers, are hard and display considerable mechanical strength. Polyallomers are prepared by copolymerization of ethylene and propylene, propylene and α-butylene, propylene and vinyl chloride or any other pair of monomers /53, 54/. The study of the structure of polyallomers by IR spectroscopy showed that the individual segments in the macromolecular chain which comprise repeating units of one of the two monomers, have a structure which is typical of the corresponding homopolymer. Polyallomers and the corresponding homopolymers of α-olefins have similar crystallinity values, unlike the products of random copolymerization, the crystallinity of which is much lower (Chapter II).

Polyallomers are distinguished from other polyolefins by a number of valuable properties. Polyallomers of propylene and ethylene are more resistant to frost than polypropylene, have a greater impact strength and possess greater resistance to notch propagation. Compared to linear medium-pressure polyethylene, they are more easily worked, have higher softening points, are harder and are more resilient to impact than linear medium-pressure polyethylene (Table 11).

TABLE 11. Properties of propylene-ethylene polyallomer, of polypropylene and of medium-pressure polyethylene /53/

Parameter	Poly-allomer	Poly-propylene	Poly-ethylene	Mixture of polypropylene with different amounts of polyethylene		
				5%	10%	15%
Density after quenching, g/cm^3	0.906	0.910	0.972	0.913	0.916	0.921
Tensile strength, kg/cm^2	224	329	217	308	308	294
Flexural strength, kg/cm^2	6,300	10,000	7,070	9,400	9,330	9,100
Elongation at break, %	>650	360	290	110	200	150
Rockwell hardness, R scale	70	93	54	91	88	83
Tensile impact strength, kg·cm/cm^2 . . .	176	70	138	77	83	97
Izod impact strength (notched specimen) . at 20°C, kg·cm/cm of notch	10.9	1.7	7.1	3.3	3.3	3.8
Izod impact strength (specimen not notched) at 23°C, kg·cm/cm	No failure	131	No failure			
Vicat softening temperature, °C	132	145	122	143	139	139
Brittleness temperature, °C	−22	+8	< −78	+1	0	−3

Polyallomers have only half as large a shrinkage as linear polyethylene. They are also superior to linear polyethylene in that they are more resistant to environmental cracking under load.

Table 12 gives the values of the most important parameters of polyallomers of propylene with α-butylene and with other monomers.

TABLE 12. Properties of propylene polyallomers /52, 53/

Parameter	Comonomer				
	α-butylene	isoprene	styrene	tetra-methyl-butadiene	vinyl chloride
Density after quenching, g/cm³	0.909	0.912	0.918	0.912	0.921
Tensile strength, kg/cm²	329	366	372	336	364
Flexural strength, kg/cm²	9,800	11,900	14,000	11,600	14,000
Elongation at break, %	225	75	—	250	—
Rockwell hardness, R scale	90	99	102	100	97
Tensile impact strength, kg·cm/cm² . . .	121	66	—	—	—
Izod impact strength (notched specimen)					
at 23°C, kg·cm/cm of notch	3.3	3.3	—	—	—
Vicat softening temperature, °C	142	147	145	145	147
Brittleness temperature, °C	− 4	− 2	>22	5	>20

It is interesting to note that if α-butylene is used as the second monomer, the polyallomer does not become more resistant to frost, as is the case when ethylene is employed in an equivalent amount.

If stereospecific catalysts are employed under conditions in which the active sites are long-lived, the resulting block copolymers consist of irregular copolymer blocks and homopolymeric stereoregular blocks. Such copolymers, which are known as stereoblock copolymers, have been prepared by copolymerization of ethylene with propylene and of ethylene with α-butylene in the presence of catalysts based on α-$TiCl_3$, $TiCl_4$, and $VOCl_3$ /50, 57/. These products are highly elastic and are more soluble than homopolymers.

The behavior of stereoblock copolymers under tensile stress differs from the behavior of products of random copolymerization and mixtures of homopolymers of the same composition. Figure 39 shows the tensile curves of an amorphous, irregular ethylene-propylene copolymer (curve 1) and of stereoblock copolymers (curves 2 and 3) of the same composition. The amorphous irregular copolymer displays a behavior which resembles that of noncrystallizing rubbers: small stresses result in large elongations, the magnitude of the latter being largely independent of the former. The stereoblock copolymer (curve 2), which is amorphous in the initial state, behaves much like crystallizing rubber on being stretched; it is assumed that at 500 − 600% elongation partial crystallization takes place, the intermolecular forces increase and so does the resistance of the material to deformation. It has been shown by X-ray studies that the orientation acquired as a result of this stretching disappears completely as soon as the load is removed. Curve 3 is typically given by stereoblock copolymers, which have a low degree of crystallinity prior to extension (3 — 15%). With regard to a comparison between stereoblock copolymers and mixtures of homopolymers, we may mention that mechanical mixtures of polypropylene and polyethylene have very small elongation coefficients, especially if their component ratio is close to unity. If such a mixture contains 50% polyethylene, its elongation is only 50 — 100% /48/.

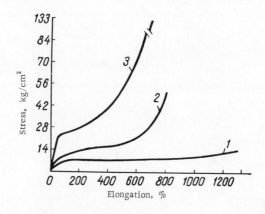

FIGURE 39. Elongation curves of ethylene
with propylene (ethylene content 50%) /50/:

1 — amorphous atactic copolymer; 2, 3 — stereoblock
copolymers.

Stereoblock copolymers are sometimes understood to include also stereoblock homopolymers /1, 55/. These are the products of stereospecific homopolymerization of propylene, α-butylene, pentene-1 /56, 57/ and some diolefins (butadiene-1,3, isoprene) /58, 59/, the macromolecules of which contain stereoregular, crystalline fragments in alternation with atactic, noncrystalline fragments. Stereoblock homopolymers are a fraction in the product of stereospecific polymerization, and have properties which are different from both the stereoregular crystalline fraction and the atactic amorphous fraction. Stereoblock homopolymers are less crystalline and lower-melting than isotactic polymers. Low-crystallinity (15 — 30%) stereoblock polymers of propylene are highly elastic and stretch reversibly up to 200% elongation. When further extended, their mechanical strength increases considerably, probably owing to the fact that they acquire orientation and isotactic segments crystallize out. Similarly to what is observed during extension of crystallizing rubbers, the crystalline regions formed as the result of the acquired orientation act in the same manner as cross-links in rubber vulcanization. However, unlike vulcanized rubbers, stereoblock polymers may be fused and molded at temperatures above the melting point of the crystalline regions. If the crystallinity of a stereoblock polymer of propylene becomes as high as 40 — 50%, its mechanical strength, stiffness and hardness all increase and the product cannot be reversibly stretched to more than 10 — 20% elongation /47/.

Block copolymers of α-olefins may also be prepared by degradation of homopolymers. If two different homopolymers are degraded at the same time, some of the macroradicals formed by chain rupture recombine in a different manner, with formation of block copolymers:

$$\cdots-A-A-A-A-\cdots \longrightarrow \cdots-A-A-\overset{\bullet}{A} \longrightarrow$$

$$\cdots-B-B-B-B-\cdots \qquad \cdots-B-B-\overset{\bullet}{B}$$

$$\longrightarrow \cdots-A-A-A-B-B-B-\cdots$$

The resulting product clearly contains not only the block copolymer, but also both homopolymers. Block copolymers are usually prepared by mechanicochemical treatment of the polymer mixture. Thus, if a mixture of polyisobutylene and low-pressure polyethylene is rolled at $165-175°C$ for 30 minutes, the corresponding block copolymer will be obtained /60/.

Block copolymers may also be prepared by degrading a polymer in the medium of some monomer. Thus, when ultrasonic waves are made to act on high-molecular, atactic polypropylene in a solution which contains styrene, a block copolymer of propylene and styrene is obtained /61/. Similar results are obtained when a polypropylene film immersed in an emulsion of another polymer is placed in an electric arc /62/.

Bibliography

1. Burlant, W. J. and A. S. Hoffman. Block and Graft Polymers. — New York, Reinhold. 1961.
2. Ceresa, R. Block and Graft Copolymers. — London, Butterworths. 1962.
3. Natta, G., E. Beati, and F. Severini. — J. Polymer Sci., 34: 685. 1959.
4. Manásek, Z., D. Berck, M. Michko, M. Lazar, and I. Pavlinets. Vysokomolekulyarnye Soedineniya, 3 (7): 1104. 1961.
5. Manásek, Z. and D. Bellus. Polipropilen (Polypropylene), p. 131, edited by V. I. Pilipovskii and I. K. Yartsev. — Izdatel'stvo "Khimiya." 1967.
6. Dudorov, V. V., A. L. Samvelyan, A. E. Lukovnikov, and P. I. Levin. — Izvestiya AN Armenskoi SSR, Khim. Nauka, 15 (4): 311. 1962.
7. Pudov, V. S. and M. B. Neiman. — In: "Starenie i stabilizatsiya polimerov," edited by A. S. Kuz'minskii, p. 5, Izdatel'stvo "Khimiya." 1966.
8. Pavlinets, I., M. Lazar, and Z. Manásek. — Khim. Volokna, No. 5: 21. 1962.
9. Manásek, Z., M. Michko, I. Pavlinets, and M. Lazar. — Khim. Volokna, No. 3: 20. 1963.
10. Konkin, A. A. and M. P. Zverev. Poliolefinovye volokna (Polyolefin Fibers), p. 242. — Izdatel'stvo "Khimiya." 1966.
11. Sirota, A. G., B. G. Fedotov, E. P. Ryabikov, P. A. Il'chenko, A. L. Gol'denberg, L. I. Zyuzina, and E. E. Manusevich. — Plast. Massy, No. 7: 10. 1967.

12. Plate, N. A. and V. P. Shibaev. — Zhurnal VKhO im. D. I. Mendeleeva, 9 (6): 637. 1964.
13. Zhunzhui, U., Z. A. Rogovin, and A. A. Konkin. — Khim. Volokna, No. 5: 18. 1961.
14. Vlasov, A. V., N. V. Mikhailov, L. G. Tokareva, S. R. Rafikov, B. L. Tsetlin, and P. Ya. Glazunov. — Khim. Volokna, No. 6: 24. 1963.
15. Tsetlin, B. L., et al. — In: "Radiatsionnaya khimiya polimerov," p. 131, Izdatel'stvo "Nauka." 1966.
16. Ryabchikova, G. G. et al. — In: "Radiatsionnaya khimiya polimerov," p. 181, Izdatel'stvo "Nauka". 1966.
17. Potts, J., E. Bonner, R. Turbett, and F. Rugg. — Am. Chem. Soc., Meeting in Minature, Jan. 1957.
18. Fedotov, B. G., A. G. Sirota, E. P. Ryabikov, P. A. Il'chenko, A. L. Gol'denberg, and O. K. Kharitonova. — Doklad na simpoziume po sintezu, pererabotke i modifikatsii poliolefinov, Baku. 1967.
19. R. W. Pearson. — Khimiya i Tekhnologiya Polimerov, No. 2: 20. 1958.
20. Lawton, E. G., J. S. Balwit, and R. S. Powell — J. Polymer Sci., 32: 257. 1958.
21. Shinohara, Y. and K. Tomioka. — J. Polymer Sci., 44 (143): 195. 1960.
22. Bevington, J. C. and D. E. Eaves. — Nature, London, 178: 1112. 1956.
23. Odian, G., T. Acker, and M. Sobel. — J. Appl. Polymer Sci., 7 (1): 245. 1963.
24. Plastics Technol., 9 (1): 53. 1963.
25. Oda, Hoshino. — Proceedings of the International Symposium on Polymers. Tokyo — Kyoto. 1966; Khimiya i Tekhnologiya Polimerov, No. 3: 5. 1967.
26. Ballantine, D. S., A. Glines, G. Adler, and D. I. Metz. — J. Polymer Sci., 34: 419. 1959.
27. Chapiro, A. — J. Polymer Sci., 29: 321. 1958.
28. Chapiro, A. — J. Polymer Sci., 34: 439. 1959.
29. Chapiro, A. — Doklad na mezhdunarodnom simpoziume po makro-molekulyarnoi khimii, Moskva. 1960.
30. Sobue, H., Y. Tazima, and Y. Shimokawa. — J. Appl. Polymer Sci., 4 (11): 244. 1960.
31. Miura, M. and S. Kawamatsu. — Chem. High Polymers (Tokyo), 19: 175. 1962.
32. Bakh, N. A. — In: "Rabot po radiatsionnoi khimii," p. 145, Izdatel'stvo AN SSSR. 1955.
33. Odor, L. and F. Gelein. — Khim. Volokna, No. 2: 18. 1961.
34. Chen, W. and H. Z. Friedlander. — Khimiya i Tekhnologiya Polimerov, No. 12: 46. 1963.
35. Oster, G. and H. Moroson. — J. Polymer Sci., 26: 233. 1957.
36. Oster, G., G. K. Oster, and H. Moroson. — J. Polymer Sci., 34 (127): 671. 1959.
37. Iwakura, N. and K. Takeda. — Proceedings of the International Symposium on Polymers, Tokyo — Kyoto. 1966; Khimiya i Tekhnologiya Polimerov, No. 3: 17. 1967.
38. Geleji, F. and L. Odor. — Khimiya i Tekhnologiya Polimerov, No. 12: 30. 1963.

39. Chapiro, A. — Proceedings of the International Symposium on Macromolecular Chemistry, Prague. 1957.

40. Lipatova, T.E., Yu.S. Lipatov, and N.L. Tutaeva. — Vysokomolekulyarnye Soedineniya, 3: 184. 1964.

41. Job, C. and P. Lebel. — Proceedings of the International Symposium on Macromolecular Chemistry, Paris. 1963.

42. Pinner, S.N. and V. Wycherley. — Plastics, 23 (244): 27. 1958.

43. Mesrobian, R.B. — Proceedings of the Second International Conference on the Peaceful Uses of Atomic Energy, Geneva. 1958. Vol. 29, p. 196.

44. Kocherginskaya, L.L., N.D. Rozenblyum, and Kh.A. Stasyuk. — Vysokomolekulyarnye Soedineniya, 4 (5): 633. 1962.

45. Rozenblyum, N.D. et al. — In: "Radiatsionnaya khimiya polimerov," p. 179, Izdatel'stvo "Nauka." 1966.

46. Klimanova, R.S., V.I. Serenkov, and N.S. Tikhomirova. — Trudy II Vsesoyuznogo soveshchaniya po radiatsionnoi khimii, p. 501, Izdatel'stvo AN SSSR. 1962.

47. Natta, G. — J. Polymer Sci., 34 (127): 531. 1959.

48. Bier, G., A. Gumboldt, and G. Lehmann. — Plastics Inst., Trans. J., 28: 98. 1960.

49. Bier, G., G. Lehmann, and H.J. Lengering. — Makromol. Chem., 44—46: 347. 1961.

50. Kontos, E.G., E.K. Easterbrook, and R.D. Gilbert.— J. Polymer Sci., 61: 69. 1962.

51. Bier, G. — Khimiya i Tekhnologiya Polimerov, No. 6: 3. 1962.

52. Pilipovskii, V.I., I.K. Yartsev, and S.A. Shibalovskaya. — Doklad na simpoziume po sintezu, pererabotke i modifikatsii poliolefinov, Baku. 1967.

53. Hagenmeyer, H.J. — Khimiya i Tekhnologiya Polimerov, No. 2: 88. 1963.

54. French Patent 1359107. 1964.

55. Natta, G., D. Mazzanti, D. Crespi, and D. Moral'o.— Khimiya i Tekhnologiya Polimerov, No. 6: 94. 1957.

56. Belgian Patent 550093. 1956.

57. Natta, G. — Khimiya i Tekhnologiya Polimerov, No. 1: 98. 1959.

58. Natta, G. — Chem. Ind. (London), No. 47: 1520. 1957.

59. Berger, M. and D. Buckley. — Chem. Eng. News, 40: 42. 1962.

60. Soviet Patent 156675. 1963; Byulleten' Izobretatelya, No. 16. 1963.

61. Romanov, A.R. and M. Lazar. — Plaste Kautschuk, No. 8: 470. 1963.

62. Belgian Patent 613561. 1962.

Chapter IV

MODIFICATION BY MEANS OF REACTIONS TAKING PLACE IN THE MACROMOLECULAR CHAIN OF POLYOLEFINS

The differences between the reactions taking place in the macromolecular chains of polyolefins and those taking place in other polymers are due, first and foremost, to the chemical inertness of polyolefins and to the existence of crystalline and amorphous regions in their structure. If the reactions are conducted in solution, and crystallinity is therefore irrelevant, the work is often difficult, since the reaction products are often insoluble in the liquids used as solvent of the initial polymers /1/. The course of the substitution reaction in the solid polymer is greatly affected by the rate of diffusion of the low-molecular reagent, which depends on the crystallinity of the polymer. As the crystallinity decreases as a result of substitution, the permeability of the polymer increases. Diffusion of a low-molecular compound which is not a solvent for the polymer, obeys Fick's Law. Diffusion of a substance which causes the polymer to swell is much faster. Regular partial substitution in the polymer is possible if the rate of the reaction is slower than the rate of diffusion of the low-molecular reagent.

Reactions in polyolefin chains are accompanied by two side processes: cross-linking and destructive degradation.

Halogenation and sulfochlorination are the two best studied reactions, by means of which functional groups can be introduced into the polyolefin macromolecule. These processes are extensively utilized in industrial practice to prepare modified types of polyethylene, both those used directly and those which serve as intermediates in further transformations, in particular vulcanization. Oxidation and thermal degradation, which are usually considered as undesirable reactions, have also been recently proposed as a means of modification of the structure and properties of polyolefins.

HALOGENATION

Halogenation of polyethylene. The chlorination of polyethylene has been studied in greatest detail. Several techniques suitable for its realization have been reported. At first it was recommended that solutions or suspensions of high-pressure polyethylene in carbon tetrachloride or acetic acid be chlorinated by gaseous chlorine in the presence of catalysts ($AlCl_3$ or $FeCl_3$) /2/. Subsequently, chlorination in the presence of titanium chloride catalyst was described /3/. The rate of the process, which shows a strong variation with the temperature, is satisfactory /4/ at about 45°C in its initial stage, and at above 55°C, after the viscosity of the reaction medium has increased. The chlorination rate can be accelerated by irradiating the reaction mixture with light of a wave length up to 4,785 Å /5, 6/. The mechanism of photochemical chlorination can be represented as follows:

$$Cl_2 \xrightarrow{h\nu} 2\dot{C}l$$

$$\dot{C}l + \cdots -CH_2 - \cdots \longrightarrow \cdots -\dot{C}H - \cdots + HCl$$

$$\cdots -\dot{C}H - \cdots + Cl_2 \longrightarrow \cdots -CHCl - \cdots + \dot{C}l$$

Since the polyolefin macromolecules contain double bonds, the chlorination obviously takes place both by addition and by substitution:

$$Cl_2 \xrightarrow{h\nu} 2\dot{C}l$$

$$R_2C = CR_2' + \dot{C}l \longrightarrow \underset{\underset{Cl}{|}}{R_2C} - \underset{\cdot}{CR_2'}$$

$$\underset{\underset{Cl}{|}}{R_2'C} - \underset{\cdot}{CR_2'} + Cl_2 \longrightarrow \underset{\underset{Cl}{|}}{R_2C} - \underset{\underset{Cl}{|}}{CR_2'} + \dot{C}l$$

Photochemical chlorination initiated by light at 20°C is accelerated in the presence of traces of oxygen which forms carbonyl groups /5/. This finding is in contradiction with other data, according to which low-temperature chlorination of paraffins is accompanied by chain termination. It is assumed that the accelerated chlorination rate is due to the formation of free macroradicals by oxidation of polyethylene /7/. Oxygen in large concentrations, on the contrary, inhibits the chlorination reaction.

Peroxy and azo compounds, which form free radicals on being heated, are used as initiators of chlorination reaction /8 − 10/.

Chlorination in suspension may be realized in different media: water, acetic acid, cold carbon tetrachloride /11/, mixture of water and carbon tetrachloride and sulfuric acid /12, 13/. It may also be realized in liquid chlorine under pressure, in which polyethylene is soluble /14, 15/.

Chlorinating agents other than chlorine can also be employed, including sulfonyl chloride /16/ and phosgene /8/.

Chlorination in solution may be performed in carbon tetrachloride. If the concentration of chlorine in solution is sufficiently high (about 7%), the reaction proceeds at a fast rate at temperatures not higher than 50°C.

Chlorination, just like bromination /17/, results in a decrease in the crystallinity of polyethylene. After the halogenation has become sufficiently advanced to produce complete amorphization, the polyethylene becomes soluble at room temperature and the reaction is continued in a homogeneous medium at relatively mild temperatures. Amorphous ethylene-propylene copolymers are also chlorinated in solution under miled temperature conditions.

Heterogeneous chlorination is accompanied by the aggregation of polymer particles which have become softened due to their diminished crystallinity. Chlorination in aqueous suspension at 65°C yields a product containing about 40% chlorine. More advanced substitution is complicated by the aggregation of the polymer particles and requires a temperature of 75°C. In order to reduce the tendency of the particles to become aggregated, the water should be saturated with hydrogen chloride or else calcium chloride should be added /18, 19/.

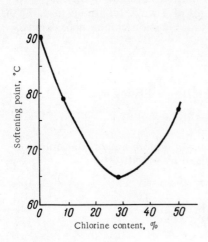

FIGURE 40. Vicat softening point under 1 kg load for polyethylene chlorinated in aqueous suspension as a function of its content of chlorine /22/.

The structure of chlorinated polyethylenes was studied by IR-spectroscopy /20, 24/. When the degree of conversion is low (less than 35% chlorine), the substitution takes place mainly at secondary carbon atoms. As the chlorine content increases, the band intensity at 660 cm^{-1} increases; this band is given by the group $-CCl_2-$, which is also noted in the spectra of poly(vinylidene chloride). On the other hand, spectra of chlorinated polyethylene containing up to 55.17% chlorine do not contain the band at 1,407 cm^{-1}, which is given by the grouping $-CH_2-CCl_2-$ /24/. If the chlorine content is about 65%, no nonchlorinated monomer links seem to be left in the polymer, since the band at 1,460 cm^{-1} disappears. The band at 722 cm^{-1}, given by four unsubstituted methylene links, disappears when the chlorine content becomes larger than 50%.

The experimental conditions are a material factor in determining the structure of the chlorinated product.

Products which have been prepared in suspension in cold carbon tetrachloride or in water, do not lose all their crystallinity and their chlorine atoms are mainly located in amorphous regions. If the chlorination is conducted in solution, the crystallinity disappears when the chlorine content is as low as 35%, while if carried out in suspension, crystalline regions remain behind even at chlorine contents of 55%.

Chlorination up to 25 — 40% chlorine content results in a decrease of the softening point of polyethylene (Figure 40), this decrease being greater for products chlorinated in solution than for those chlorinated in suspension /22/. If the chlorine content is raised further, the softening temperature increases despite the fact that the product is then largely amorphous, probably owing to the intensification of intermolecular forces. Curves showing the tensile strength and the hardness of chlorinated polyethylene as a function of its chlorine content also have a minimum (Figure 41). The increase in the values of these parameters at chlorine contents higher than those corresponding to their minimum values (35 — 45% Cl) is due to the increase in the intermolecular forces, which more than offsets the loss of crystallinity /7/. Polyethylene chlorinated in suspension retains some of its crystallinity, and is accordingly stiffer than polyethylene chlorinated in solution with the same degree of substitution /11, 19, 25/. Polyethylene chlorinated in suspension is not as soluble as the product chlorinated in solution.

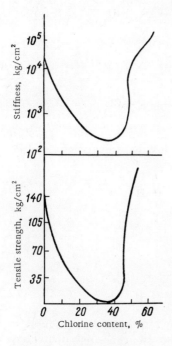

FIGURE 41. Tensile strength and stiffness of chlorinated polyethylene as a function of its chlorine content /25/.

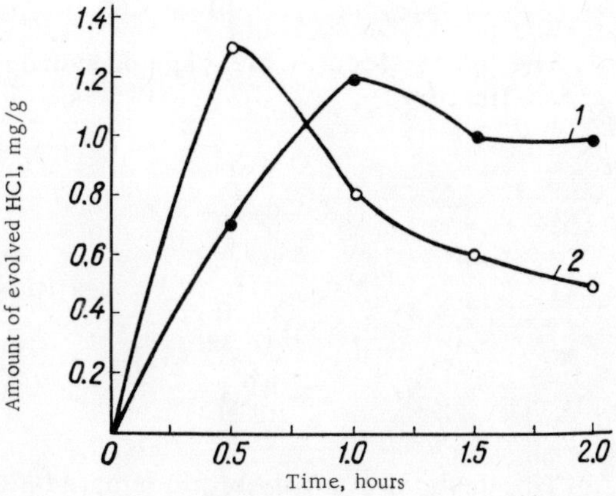

FIGURE 42. Thermal stability of chlorinated polyethylene containing 60% chlorine (1) and of unstabilized poly(vinyl chloride) (2) at 160°C /26/.

The valuable property of chlorinated polyethylene — its low flammability — also depends on its method of preparation. If the chlorination is carried out in suspension, the product becomes fire-proof at a chlorine content as low as 25%, while polyethylene chlorinated in solution loses its flammability when its chlorine content attains about 40%. The reason for this is the deposition of a highly chlorinated layer of polymer particles on the surface of the polymer which has been chlorinated in suspension.

The thermal stability of chlorinated polyethylene is somewhat lower than that of poly(vinyl chloride), as measured by the amount of hydrogen chloride evolved when the polymer is heated (Figure 42). The activation energy of thermal decomposition of polyethylene containing 55.17% chlorine between 135 and 168°C is 7.1 kcal/mole /27/. The low activation energy of dehydrochlorination reaction, in conjunction with the fact that inhibitors of free radical reactions are without effect on the thermal decomposition, made it possible to propose an ionic mechanism of cleavage of hydrogen chloride as a result of the polarizing effect of the chlorine atoms; these induce positive charges on α- and β-carbon atoms, thus facilitating the cleavage of hydrogen atoms /27/:

$$\cdots -\underset{\underset{H}{|}}{\overset{\overset{H}{|}}{\underset{\beta}{C}}}{}^{\delta+}-\underset{\underset{Cl^{\delta-}}{|}}{\overset{\overset{H}{|}}{\underset{\alpha}{C}}}{}^{\delta+}\cdots \longrightarrow \cdots -\underset{|}{\overset{\overset{H}{|}}{C}}-\underset{\underset{Cl}{|}}{\overset{\overset{H}{|}}{C}}-\cdots +H^+$$

A chlorine ion splits off the macroanion formed:

$$\cdots -{}^-\underset{|}{\overset{\overset{H}{|}}{C}}-\underset{\underset{Cl}{|}}{\overset{\overset{H}{|}}{C}}-\cdots \longrightarrow \cdots -\overset{\overset{H}{|}}{C}=\overset{\overset{H}{|}}{C}-\cdots +Cl^-$$

The intermolecular cleavage of hydrogen chloride is accompanied by cross-linking:

$$
\begin{array}{ccc}
\cdots -\underset{\underset{H^+\;Cl}{|\;\;\;|}}{\overset{\overset{H\;\;H}{|\;\;|}}{C-C}}- \cdots & & \cdots -\underset{\underset{Cl}{|}}{\overset{\overset{H\;\;H}{|\;\;|}}{C-C}}- \cdots \\
& \longrightarrow \;HCl+ & \;\;| \\
\cdots -\underset{\underset{H\;\;H}{|\;\;|}}{\overset{\overset{Cl^-\;H}{|\;\;\;|}}{C-C}}- \cdots & & \cdots -\underset{\underset{H\;\;H}{|\;\;|}}{\overset{\overset{H}{|}}{C-C}}- \cdots
\end{array}
$$

The thermal stability of chlorinated polyethylene (and of poly(vinyl chloride)) is enhanced by the introduction of stabilizers, which neutralize the hydrogen chloride evolved on heating /11/.

Chlorinated polyethylene has its own specific uses, including protective coatings and in compounding with poly(vinyl chloride). If chlorinated polyethylene is introduced into poly(vinyl chloride), in even small amounts, the brittleness of the latter polymer at low temperatures decreases, and the working temperature range is increased correspondingly.

Once chlorine atoms have been introduced into polyethylene, other derivatives can also be prepared by realizing suitable reactions in the macromolecular chain. Thus, when low-pressure chlorinated polyethylene is made to react with aniline, dibutylamine and aqueous ammonia, aminated products are obtained /27, 28/. The main reactions involved are dehydrochlorination, which results in the formation of double bonds in the chain, the substitution of some of the chlorine atoms by amino groups and intermolecular cross-linking:

$$\cdots -CH_2-CHCl- \cdots \xrightarrow{NH_3} \cdots -CH=CH- \cdots +NH_3\cdot HCl$$

$$\cdots -CH=CH- \cdots \xrightarrow{NH_3} \cdots -\underset{\underset{NH_2}{|}}{CH_2-CH}-\cdots$$

$$\cdots -\underset{\underset{NH_2}{|}}{CH_2-CH}- \cdots + \cdots -CH=CH- \cdots \longrightarrow \cdots -\underset{\underset{NH}{|}}{CH_2-CH}- \cdots$$
$$\underset{\cdots -CH_2-\overset{|}{C}H- \cdots}{}$$

Bromine vigorously reacts with polyethylene. It is assumed that bromine adds onto macroradicals more rapidly than chlorine /1/. The ratio between the respective amounts of chlorine and bromine required to modify the properties of polyethylene in the same manner is close to the ratio of their atomic weights. Polyethylene containing 55% bromine is a rubber-like substance; polyethylene containing 71.5% bromine is stiff, while polyethylene containing 86% bromine is hard and brittle /2/.

Fluorination of polyethylene proceeds at a vigorous rate, with evolution of a large amount of heat. It is recommended that fluorine be diluted with an inert gas in order to reduce the rate of reaction and minimize the degradation of the polymer. If a polymer in the form of a film or a powder is treated with a nitrogen-fluorine mixture in the dark, 10% fluorine can be introduced into the polymer while maintaining a moderate rate of reaction; the product is not degraded /29, 30/. In order to prevent violent fluorination which is accompanied by carbonization or combustion of polyethylene, the process may be conducted in the presence of nonreactive metals such as copper, nickel or phosphorous bronze. The resulting products may have differing degrees of substitution, up to 76% fluorine, which corresponds to the full substitution. Fully fluorinated polyethylene is much like polytetrafluoroethylene in its properties. X-ray studies showed that it structurally resembles polytetrafluoroethylene with a very low degree of crystallinity /31/.

Halogenation of polypropylene and other polyolefins. Polypropylene, like polyethylene, may be halogenated in solution, in suspension, and in the form of powder.

Chlorination in solution is carried out using chlorinated hydrocarbons (carbon tetrachloride, chloroform, chlorobenzene, dichlorobenzene, etc.) as solvents. The course of the reaction largely depends on the structure of the initial polymer. Homogeneous chlorination is only possible if an atactic polypropylene is employed. Polypropylene containing a stereoregular fraction is dissolved only partly, the crystalline fraction merely swelling in the solvent. As the surface layers of the crystalline fraction become chlorinated, the fraction passes into solution. If the content of chlorine in the polymers exceeds 40%, the polymer is fully soluble and a uniformly substituted product is obtained. If the chlorine content is smaller, a mixture is obtained, consisting of the soluble polymer which is more highly substituted, and a gel which is less highly substituted /32/.

The effect of the temperature on the degree of substitution also depends on the structure of the polymer. Figure 43 shows the contents of chlorine in a stereoblock polypropylene, in an isotactic polypropylene and in a low-pressure polyethylene as a function of the chlorination temperature /24/. If the chlorination temperature of a stereoblock polypropylene containing 32% of amorphous fraction, soluble in cold heptane, is raised from 5 to 25°C, the chlorine content gradually increases. Further increase in temperature has no significant effect on the degree of conversion. Chlorination of highly crystalline isotactic polypropylene (content of amorphous fraction soluble in cold heptane 3.7%), and of low-pressure polyethylene is insigificant below 25°C. It would appear that only the soluble amorphous fraction of the polymer is chlorinated under these conditions. If the reaction temperature is raised to 40°C, the chlorine content in the crystalline fractions increases considerably, probably as a result of the chlorination and dissolution of the surface layers of the crystalline formations.

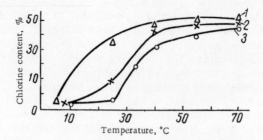

FIGURE 43. Chlorine content as a function of the temperature of chlorination of stereoblock polypropylene (1), isotactic polypropylene (2) and low-pressure polyethylene (3) /24/.

The chlorination rate increases considerably in the presence of peroxides /33/ and azo compounds /34/. Figure 44 shows the acceleration in the chlorination rate of a polypropylene specimen containing 45% of the isotactic fraction in the presence of azoisobutyric acid dinitrile.

The chlorination rate increases as a result of irradiation with light in the wavelength range 2,000 — 6,500 Å. Krentsel' et al. /34/ studied the photochemical chlorination of polypropylene containing about 60% of isotactic fraction in carbon tetrachloride at 20 — 25°C and obtained products containing up to 62% chlorine. It is interesting to note that the chlorination of polyethylene under the same mild conditions results in the introduction of not more than 20% chlorine. This is probably due to the presence of tertiary carbon atoms in the polypropylene macromolecules, the hydrogen on which is readily substituted by chlorine.

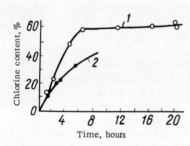

FIGURE 44. Kinetic chlorination curves of polypropylene containing 45% of the isotactic fraction in the presence (1) and absence (2) of azoisobutyric acid dinitrile initiator at 75—80°C /34/.

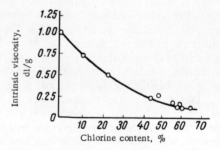

FIGURE 45. Variation of intrinsic viscosity of polypropylene during chlorination /34/.

The chlorination of polypropylene, just like the chlorination of polyethylene /24/, results in some degradation of the polymer chains /34, 36/. This is indicated by the decreasing intrinsic viscosity of the polymer with its increasing chlorine content (Figure 45). If TiCl$_4$ is used as catalyst, the extent of degradation may be reduced /3/.

Chlorination of polypropylene in suspension at temperatures between 60 and 105°C yields homogeneous products, containing about 60% chlorine. Water, glacial acetic acid, aqueous acetic acid /37/ and hydrochloric acid /18, 38/ may serve as reaction media. Thus, for instance, polypropylene, polyethylene and ethylene-propylene copolymers may be efficiently chlorinated by passing gaseous chlorine through a suspension of the polymer in concentrated hydrochloric acid, the reaction mixture being irradiated with 2,500 — 6,000 Å light. If it is desired to obtain a product with a chlorine content exceeding 50%, the reaction is first conducted at a moderate temperature (75 — 95°C) until the product contains about 50% chlorine, after which the chlorination is continued at 95 — 105°C. If concentrated HCl is used, aggregation of polymer particles is prevented /18/.

The suspension method is also successfully employed in the chlorination of poly-4-methylpentene-1 /37, 39/. However, the resulting degradation of this polymer was much more extensive than that of polyethylene chlorinated under similar conditions.

Chlorination of polypropylene powder by dry chlorine /37, 40 — 42/ proceeds at a more rapid rate. The activation energy of the reaction is 4.8 kcal/mole /40, 42/. If the process is carried out in the dark and in the presence of sodium chloride, the extent of degradation can be reduced /40/. Under these conditions the content of chlorine may attain 25.8%, while the melting point and the crystallinity are not significantly changed.

The bromination of polypropylene takes place in daylight in a solution of bromine in chlorinated hydrocarbons (carbon tetrachloride, dichlorobenzene, etc.), in a manner similar to chlorination /40, 43, 44/. The activation energy of the bromination process is 11.4 kcal/mole /40/.

Brominated polypropylene is unstable and evolves hydrogen bromide at room temperature. Chlorinated polypropylene is more stable, but hydrogen chloride is evolved on heating. If the chlorine content is about 60%, hydrogen chloride is evolved at 108°C and above. If stabilizers, such as are used in the stabilization of poly(vinyl chloride), are employed, the decomposition temperature of chlorinated polypropylene becomes much higher. Thus, it becomes 171 — 173°C in the presence of 4% calcium stearate and 188°C in the presence of lead silicate /34/.

Thermal degradation of chlorinated polypropylene was studied /27, 45/ as a function of its chlorine content. It was shown that the maximum degradation occurs when the chlorine content is 45.7% (Figure 46). This closely corresponds to one substituted hydrogen atom in each monomer link. Similar data were obtained for the thermal degradation of poly-α-butylene /27/.

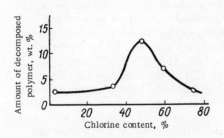

FIGURE 46. Thermal degradation at 120°C of chlorinated polypropylene as a function of its chlorine content (duration of heating, 200 minutes) /45/.

It was found /45/ that the dehydrochlorination of chlorinated polypropylene proceeds at a variable rate. Between 100 and 238°C the decomposition rate remained constant for 10 — 20 minutes, after which it decreased and no more hydrogen chloride was evolved at the given temperature.

This finding is explained by postulating two different dehydrochlorination mechanisms, an intramolecular mechanism:

$$
\cdots-CH_2-\underset{\underset{Cl}{|}}{\overset{\overset{CH_3}{|}}{C}}-CH_2-\underset{\underset{H}{|}}{\overset{\overset{CH_3}{|}}{C}}-\cdots \longrightarrow HCl + \cdots-CH_2-\underset{}{\overset{\overset{CH_3}{|}}{C}}=CH-\underset{\underset{H}{|}}{\overset{\overset{CH_3}{|}}{C}}-\cdots
$$

and an intermolecular mechanism:

$$
\cdots-CH_2-\underset{\underset{Cl}{|}}{\overset{\overset{CH_3}{|}}{C}}-CH_2-\underset{\underset{H}{|}}{\overset{\overset{CH_3}{|}}{C}}-\cdots + \cdots-CH_2-\underset{\underset{H}{|}}{\overset{\overset{CH_3}{|}}{C}}-CH_2-\underset{\underset{Cl}{|}}{\overset{\overset{CH_3}{|}}{C}}-\cdots \longrightarrow
$$

$$
\cdots-CH_2-\underset{}{\overset{\overset{CH_3}{|}}{C}}-CH_2-\underset{\underset{H}{|}}{\overset{\overset{CH_3}{|}}{C}}-\cdots
$$

$$
\longrightarrow HCl + \quad\quad\quad | \quad\quad\quad\quad |
$$

$$
\cdots-CH_2-\underset{\underset{CH_3}{|}}{\overset{\overset{Cl}{|}}{C}}-CH_2-\underset{\underset{CH_3}{|}}{\overset{}{C}}-\cdots
$$

It is known that the activation energy of the latter process is smaller than that of the former, but the former process has a higher probability of occurrence. It follows that at relatively low temperatures the intermolecular dehydrochlorination mechanism will predominate. As the temperature is increased, more hydrogen chloride will be evolved by the intramolecular mechanism. As the cross-linking of the polymer advances as a result of intermolecular cleavage acts, the dehydrochlorination becomes more difficult and, after the density of the cross links has attained a certain minimum value, the process ceases altogether at this temperature. At high temperatures (250°C) the evolution of HCl is accompanied by degradation of the polymer chains, with evolution of gaseous hydrocarbon products, and the overall rate of decomposition of the polymer becomes much higher than at temperatures around 100°C.

These ideas account for the shape of the curve (Figure 46) giving the extent of degradation of chlorinated polypropylene as a function of its chlorine content. At relatively low temperatures chlorine contents of up to 30% have practically no effect on the thermal stability of chlorinated polypropylene, since the polymer has then attained a certain degree of cross-linking. If the chlorine content is increased above 30%, i.e., to a content of more than 1 chlorine atom per 2 repeating monomer units, the rate of dehydrochlorination increases rapidly, since the introduction of a chlorine atom into a monomeric link enhances the mobility of hydrogen atoms in the neighboring links /46/.

If the chlorination is continued past a chlorine content of 46.5% (i. e., after all the hydrogens on tertiary carbon atoms have been substituted), hydrogens in methylene and methyl groups begin to be substituted /46/. The number of mobile hydrogen atoms decreases, and the chlorination product becomes more thermostable (right side of curve in Figure 46).

The activation energy of dehydrochlorination of chlorinated polypropylene is small — only about 8 kcal/mole /45/ — while that of the chlorinated poly-α-butylene is 6.4 kcal/mole /27/. Since the value of this activation energy is much smaller than that required to break the C—C bonds in the macromolecular chains and is much too small for the dehydrochlorination reaction to proceed by a free radical mechanism, and since this reaction takes place at a relatively low temperature (100°C), it follows that the thermal degradation of the chlorinated polypropylene proceeds by an ionic mechanism /46/. (Poly(vinyl chloride), which is degraded by a free radical mechanism, begins to evolve hydrogen chloride above 140°C, and the activation energy of the decomposition is 36.5 kcal/mole /47, 48/). It is possible that the degradation which proceeds according to an ionic mechanism originates from the residue of the polymerization catalyst contained in the chlorinated polypropylene.

Similarly to the thermal degradation of chlorinated polyethylene, the thermal degradation of chlorinated polypropylene may be described as follows:

$$
\begin{array}{ccc}
\text{H} & \text{CH}_3 & \\
|^{\delta+} |^{\delta+} & & \\
\cdots\!-\!\text{C}\!-\!\text{C}\!-\!\cdots & \longrightarrow & \cdots\text{C}\!-\!\text{C}\!-\!\cdots + \text{H}^+ \\
| & | & \\
\text{H} & \text{Cl}^{\delta-} & \text{Cl}
\end{array}
$$

$$
\begin{array}{ccc}
\text{H} & \text{CH}_3 & \\
| & | & \\
\cdots\!-\!\text{C}\!-\!\text{C}\!-\! & \longrightarrow & \cdots\!-\!\text{C}\!=\!\text{C}\!-\!\cdots + \text{Cl}^- \\
| & & \\
& \text{Cl}^{\delta-} &
\end{array}
$$

The cross-linking may be represented as follows:

$$
\begin{array}{ccc}
\text{H} \quad \text{CH}_3 & & \text{H} \quad \text{CH}_3 \\
\cdots\!-\!\text{C}\!-\!\text{C}\!-\!\cdots & & \cdots\!-\!\text{C}\!-\!\text{C}\!-\!\cdots \\
|^{\delta+}\;\; & & | \\
\text{H} \quad \text{Cl} & \longrightarrow & \text{Cl} \\
+ & & \qquad\qquad + \text{HCl} \\
\text{Cl}^{\delta-} \;\text{H} & & \text{H} \\
\cdots\!-\!\text{C}\!-\!\text{C}\!-\!\cdots & & \cdots\!-\!\text{C}\!-\!\text{C}\!-\!\cdots \\
\text{CH}_3 \; \text{H} & & \text{CH}_3\,\text{H}
\end{array}
$$

That dehydrochlorination is in fact accompanied by cross-linking is shown by the decreased solubility of the polymer and by the relatively small density of cross-links /46/.

Chlorination of polypropylene takes place mostly in amorphous regions, as evidenced, for example, by the higher chlorination rate of less crystalline polymers. However, in order to attain higher degrees of substitution, the reaction must also take place in crystalline regions. The content of the isotactic fraction decreases with increasing degree of chlorination, possibly owing to rearrangements taking place at the asymmetric tertiary carbon atoms /34, 35/, the hydrogen of which is the first to be substituted by chlorine. It is believed that the effect of such rearrangements is much stronger than the effect of electrostatic repulsion between the chlorine atoms which have replaced hydrogen in methyl groups.

The melting point of chlorinated products containing small amounts of chlorine is lower than that of the initial polymers /34, 35, 37/. If the chlorine content is increased beyond 10 − 20%, the melting point increases rapidly, and the density of the polypropylene increases as well.

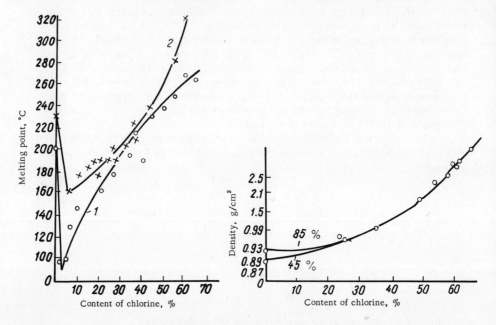

FIGURE 47. Melting points of chlorinated poly-propylene (1) and poly-4-methylpentene-1 (2) as a function of their chlorine contents /37/.

FIGURE 48. Density of chlorinated polypropylene as a function of its chlorine content, at different contents of the isotactic fraction /34/.

Figure 47 shows typical curves representing the variation of the melting points of chlorinated polypropylene and poly-4-methylpentene-1 as a function of their chlorine content. The relationship between the degree of chlorination and density is shown in Figure 48. Polypropylene which has undergone advanced chlorination is brittle and is not flammable. It was shown by thermomechanical investigations /34/ that if the chlorine content is higher than 45%, the polypropylene has no highly elastic range and, on being heated, passes from the vitreous state directly to the visco-fluid state.

Elastomers stable to the action of ozone can be prepared from poly-propylene containing more than 20% chlorine by reacting it with magnesium, lead and zinc oxides /36, 41, 49, 50/. Surface chlorination of articles made of polypropylene enhances their takeup of dyes, printing colors, adhesives and photographic emulsions /51, 54/. Chlorinated polypropylene may be used in bonding various materials, in particular poly(vinyl chloride) and poly(vinylene chloride) /55/.

SULFOCHLORINATION

The utilization of chlorinated polyolefins in the preparation of vulcanized materials is limited in scope. Sulfochlorinated polyolefins are much more suitable for this purpose /1, 7, 11, 56 − 58/, owing to the considerable reactivity of sulfonyl chloride groups.

Sulfochlorination of polyethylene. Sulfochlorination of polyethylene is most often effected by the use of a mixture of chlorine with sulfur dioxide:

$$\cdots-CH_2-CH_2-CH_2-CH_2-\cdots + 2Cl_2 + SO_2 \longrightarrow$$
$$\longrightarrow \cdots-\underset{\underset{Cl}{|}}{CH}-CH_2-CH_2-\underset{\underset{O=\underset{\underset{Cl}{|}}{S}=O}{|}}{CH}-\cdots + 2HCl$$

The experimental conditions employed are similar to those used in chlorination. Since the reaction proceeds by a chain radical mechanism, it can be initiated by peroxides or azo compounds /59/ or by irradiation /60, 61/. The usual procedure is to effect a photochemically initiated sulfochlorination of polyethylene dissolved in carbon tetrachloride at 60 − 75°C. The rubberlike product contains 20 − 45% chlorine and 0.4 − 3% sulfur. The ratio between the contents of chloride and sulfonyl chloride groups is adjusted by varying the mutual proportions of chlorine and sulfur dioxide in the initial gas mixture /62/ and by varying the reaction temperature /63 − 65/. The ratio between sulfonyl chloride and chloride groups in the product will be higher, the higher the sulfur dioxide:chlorine ratio in the gas mixture and the lower the sulfochlorination temperature.

Previously prepared sulfuryl chloride may be employed as the sulfochlorination agent /61/. The reaction is catalyzed by pyridine, thiophenols and other similar substances, capable of forming complexes with sulfuryl chloride and with the hydrogen chloride which is evolved /36/. It is believed /1/ that the sulfone radicals, formed as intermediate products, become stabilized by the formation of complexes with pyridine, pyridinium ion or complex of pyridine with sulfuryl chloride:

$$RH + \dot{C}l \xrightarrow[-HCl]{} \dot{R}-\begin{cases} \overset{SO_2}{\underset{}{\rightleftharpoons}} R\dot{S}O_2 \xrightarrow{Cl_2} RSO_2Cl + \dot{C}l \\ \xrightarrow{Cl_2} RCl + \dot{C}l \end{cases}$$

If sulfuryl chloride is used in conjunction with free radical initiators such as peroxides, chlorination becomes the main reaction /7/. In the capacity of sulfochlorination agent, sulfuryl chloride has no advantages over mixtures of chlorine with sulfur dioxide.

Sulfochlorination may also be effected under heterogeneous conditions. Thus, if a fine powder of low-pressure polyethylene, molecular weight 80,000, is treated with a chlorine − sulfur dioxide mixture at 40 − 80°C, the product will consist of sulfochlorinated polyethylene containing 18% chlorine and 3.2% sulfur /64/.

The sulfochlorination products are unstable to heat and light. The decomposition is accompanied by the evolution of hydrogen chloride and sulfur dioxide. The recommended stabilizing agents include: α- and β-pinenes /66/, phenyl glycidyl ether /67/, propylene oxide with gelatin and octylphenol /68/.

One of the most important varieties of sulfochlorinated polyethylene, the so-called Hypalon, is mainly used as vulcanizable elastomer /11, 25, 69/. It is prepared from polyethylene with a molecular weight of about 20,000. The chlorine content of Hypalon is $26-29\%$, while the content of sulfur is $1.3-1.7\%$. One chlorine atom in the product occurs about every 7 carbon atoms, while one sulfonyl chloride group appears every 90 carbon atoms /25, 69, 70/. The sulfonyl chloride groups mainly add onto the secondary carbon atoms: the chlorine atoms which do not form part of sulfonyl chloride groups are distributed in the chain in a random manner and are bound to primary, secondary and tertiary carbon atoms /71- 74/. Thus, for instance, a product of sulfochlorination of high-pressure polyethylene by a mixture of chlorine with SO_2 in CCl_4 was found to contain 31% chlorine and 1.2% sulfur; 2.7% of the chlorine atoms were bound to primary carbon atoms, 89.8% to the secondary, 3.5% to the tertiary, while 4% formed part of sulfonyl chloride groups /75/. Clearly, the sulfo-chlorination of linear polyethylenes, which are practically free from branchings and methyl groups, yields products in which the proportion of chlorine bound to secondary carbon atoms is even higher.

Sulfochlorinated polyethylene decomposes on being heated to $125-150°C$, with the evolution of SO_2 and HCl:

$$RCH_2CHR' \longrightarrow RCH{=}CHR' + SO_2 + HCl$$
$$\underset{SO_2}{|}$$

The resulting double bonds may be employed in sulfur vulcanization.

The most important property of the sulfochlorinated polyethylene is that it can be vulcanized and that this vulcanization involves the sulfonyl chloride groups. These groups react with metal oxides to form salts, and react with bifunctional amines to give sulfamide groups. Vulcanization by diamines, dimercaptans and other compounds, which results in the liberation of hydrogen chloride, may also involve the participation of chlorine atoms, especially those attached to tertiary carbon atoms.

Nonvulcanized, sulfochlorinated polyethylene of the Hypalon type is a rubberlike material, which remains elastic to $-45°C$. It is highly resistant to the action of ozone. Owing to its high chlorine content, it is much more resistant to fire than other elastomers. It is soluble in aromatic and chlorinated hydrocarbons and can thus be employed as varnish. It is also used in rubber compounding.

Sulfochlorination of polypropylene. Like polyethylene, polypropylene is sulfochlorinated by mixtures of chlorine with sulfur dioxide. The reaction can be performed under homogeneous or under heterogeneous conditions. In the former case methylene chloride, carbon tetrachloride, chloroform, tetrachloroethane and hexachloroethane may be used as solvents /35, $76-78/$.

The reaction rate is increased by exposing the mixture to light or to γ-radiation /76, 79/. The rate of sulfochlorination depends on how regular the structure of the polymer is: the more regular the polymer, the slower the reaction rate /80/. At a certain degree of regularity the reaction medium is no longer homogeneous; homogeneity is also lost if the degree of sulfochlorination is advanced, owing to partial cross-linking of the macromolecular chains by sulfonyl chloride groups.

In the absence of a solvent, polypropylene is mainly sulfochlorinated in the amorphous regions. At higher crystallinities the reaction rate decreases. The magnitude of the activation energy of the process varies with the degree of conversion of the polypropylene. In the presence of 93% unreacted hydrogen the energy of activation is 25 kcal/mole; in the presence of 82.9% hydrogen it is 44 kcal/mole /81/. Heterogeneous sulfochlorination can be performed continuously in counter-current /81/ or in fluidized bed layer /82/.

The reaction is accompanied by a decrease in the intrinsic viscosity of the polymer, which is higher, the higher the content of chlorine and especially the higher the content of sulfur in the product /76/. If the sulfur content is 1−2%, the sulfochlorinated polypropylene remains highly elastic throughout the temperature range between the vitrification point and the temperature which corresponds to incipient cross-linking. If the sulfur dioxide : chlorine ratio in the reaction mixture and the experimental conditions are varied, different products may be obtained. Thus, at a chlorine content of 37%, a crystalline product, a rubber with working temperature range of 150−190°C, or a hard cross-linked material may be obtained by varying the sulfur content from zero to 6%. Sulfochlorinated polypropylene is readily soluble in chlorinated and in aromatic hydrocarbons. When heated above 110°C, and when exposed to UV light, it decomposes with the evolution of hydrogen chloride and sulfur dioxide. It can be stabilized by the agents used in the stabilization of poly(vinyl chloride). The main industrial application of sulfochlorinated polypropylene is in the capacity of the starting product for vulcanization. Other uses of sulfochlorinated polypropylene are also known /32/. Sulfochlorination of polypropylene films improves their adhesive properties, while the sulfochlorination of fibers improves their affinity to basic dyes.

PHOSPHORYLATION

When polyethylene is made to react with PCl_3 in the presence of oxygen, phosphonyl chloride groups are introduced into the macromolecular polyethylene chain /83/:

$$\cdots-CH_2-CH_2-CH_2-CH_2-\cdots + PCl_3 + 1/2O_2 \longrightarrow$$

$$\longrightarrow \cdots-CH_2-CH-CH_2-CH_2-\cdots + HCl$$

$$\underset{\underset{O}{\overset{\|}{\underset{\displaystyle}{}}}}{\overset{|}{Cl-P-Cl}}$$

The reaction is conducted at 50°C and above, since phosphorus trichloride dissolves polyethylene at these temperatures. The phosphorylation rate depends on the oxygen content in the reaction medium. The process, which takes place by a free radical mechanism, is initiated by peroxide compounds. The presence of double bonds in the polyethylene accelerates the rate of phosphorylation, probably owing to the reaction:

$$\text{C}{=}\text{C} + PCl_3 + {}^{1}\!/_{2}O_2 \longrightarrow \ -\overset{|}{\underset{Cl}{C}}\!\!-\!\!-\!\!-\overset{|}{\underset{Cl-\overset{\displaystyle O}{\underset{\|}{P}}-Cl}{C}}-$$

The phosphorylated polyethylene is readily hydrolyzed:

$$\cdots{-}CH_2{-}\underset{\underset{O}{\overset{\|}{\underset{}{}}}}{\overset{\displaystyle|}{\underset{Cl-P-Cl}{CH}}}{-}CH_2{-}\cdots + 2H_2O \longrightarrow \cdots{-}CH_2{-}\underset{\underset{O}{\overset{\|}{}}}{\overset{\displaystyle|}{\underset{HO-P-OH}{CH}}}{-}CH_2{-}\cdots + 2HCl$$

If the phosphorus content is sufficiently high (15.5% /84/), the products of the hydrolysis are fully soluble in water. The products can be cross-linked by reaction with a metal oxide, such as lead oxide. Schroeder et al. /83/ studied the various derivatives of phosphorylated polyethylene (diethyl ether and other ethers, amide-containing products, etc.).

Bellush et al. /85/ studied the phosphorylation of atactic polypropylene. The reaction was performed in a solution of the polymer in phosphorus trichloride in the presence of oxygen at $50-55°C$. According to the authors, the substitution mainly takes place at the tertiary carbon atoms. The content of phosphorus in the hydrolyzed product attained 7.2% (11.7 $-PO(OH)_2$ groups per 100 repeating units). As the phosphorylation proceeds, the solubility in hot hydrocarbon solvents (toluene, etc.) diminishes, while the solubility in polar solvents (ethyl acetate, etc.) increases. Phosphorylated polypropylene becomes more hydrophilic with increasing degree of conversion (Figure 49).

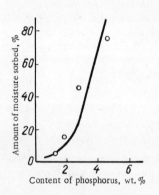

FIGURE 49. Effect of the degree of phosphorylation of atactic polypropylene on the adsorption of water vapor (relative humidity 100%, temperature 20°C, duration 7 days) /85/.

The surface of films, fibers and other articles made of polypropylene can be phosphorylated after the article has been previously allowed to swell in PCl_3 or in a solution of PCl_3 in an organic solvent /32, p. 139/.

Hydrolyzed phosphorylated polypropylenes, like hydrolyzed phosphorylated polyethylenes, may become cross-linked by oxides of bivalent metals /86/. The vulcanized product thus obtained is highly resistant to ozone, can act as ion exchanger and is resistant to fire.

If the $-PO(OH)_2$ groups in the surface are converted to amides or esters /87/, the polypropylene product will acquire increased resistance to heat and light, improved dye takeup and higher capacity to act as an ion exchanger.

A vulcanized product has been obtained /88, 89/ by phosphorylating an ethylene-propylene copolymer.

Phosphorylation of polyisobutylene under conditions employed in the phosphorylation of polyethylene yields a highly degraded product, whose degree of phosphorylation is insignificant /1/.

OXIDATION

Extensive literature is available on the oxidation of polyolefins /1, 90, 91/. Most of these publications deal with the suppression of oxidative degradation processes during the conversion of the polyolefin to the finished article and during the service life of the article. However, oxidation has been recently employed as a means of modification of the polyolefin. Oxidation of polyethylene during heating makes it possible to introduce oxygenated groups into the macromolecule, mainly carbonyl, hydroperoxy and ester groups /92, 93/. Photochemical oxidation is accompanied mainly by the formation of carbonyl groups and by the increase in the content of vinyl groups and internal double bonds /21, 92/. The appearance of carbonyl groups greatly enhances the absorption of UV light (around 2,800 Å) by polyethylene. Photolysis of carbonyl-containing oxidation products results in the formation of free radicals, which are capable of initiating oxidative chain processes, with possible formation of hydroperoxy groups /94/:

$$\dot{R} \xrightarrow{O_2} R\dot{O}O \xrightarrow{RH} ROOH + \dot{R}$$

Heterogeneous oxidation of polyethylene below the melting point of the crystalline phase is faster, the lower the crystallinity (Figure 50) /95/. Under these conditions the oxidation mainly takes place in the amorphous regions, in which oxygen diffuses at a much more rapid rate than in the crystalline phase. This is proved by the fact that crystallinity is retained during the oxidation of polyethylene below its melting point /1/. The difference between the rates of oxidation of the branched and the linear polyethylene, which is due to their different crystallinities, disappears if the oxidation is carried out in the melt (Figure 51) /95/. Thus, the oxidation rate is determined by the crystallinity of the polymer and not by its activity which increases with increasing degree of branching.

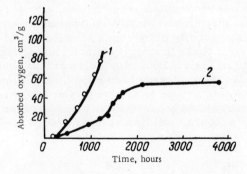

FIGURE 50. Kinetic oxidation curves of branched (curve 1, density 0.920 g/cm^3) and linear (curve 2, density 0.958 g/cm^3) polyethylene at 80°C /95/.

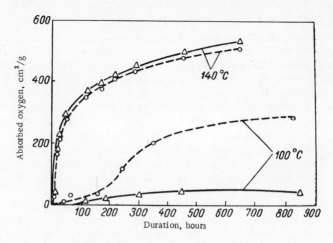

FIGURE 51. Kinetic oxidation curves of polyethylene above and below the melting point /95/:

------ —branched polyethylene, density 0.920 g/cm³; ———— — linear polyethylene, density 0.958 g/cm³.

Of major interest is the oxidation of polyethylene to products containing carboxyl groups. A treatment of molten polyethylene in the air at 160 — 200°C with the aid of roller mills for several hours /96/ yielded a carboxylated polymer containing 0.1 — 0.5 wt. % of oxygen. The oxidation can also be effected by oxidizing agents such as nitric acid. If polyethylene is treated with 35 — 85% solution of nitric acid at 70 — 130°C for several hours, the main products are dicarboxylic acids with molecular weights between 250 and 1,000 /8/. Polyethylene is efficiently oxidized by an ozone-oxygen mixture in CCl₄ at 70 — 78°C; the main products are hydroxydicarboxylic acids with molecular weights between 100 and 2,000.

Due to its capacity to form stable water emulsions, carboxylated polyethylene is mainly used in textile impregnations, etc. /11/.

Polypropylene is much more readily oxidized than polyethylene. This is due to the higher reactivity of hydrogen atoms attached to tertiary carbon atoms, as compared to those in methyl or methylene groups /97/.

Hydroperoxidations, carried out with a view to subsequent grafting on the resulting active sites, have already been mentioned. Minsker et al. /98/ reduced the hydroperoxy groups to hydroxyls. One of the possible techniques is to treat hydroperoxydated polypropylene with a solution of potassium iodide at 20°C for 6 hours. All hydroperoxy groups are then converted to hydroxyls as follows:

$$
\cdots\text{—}\underset{\underset{\text{OOH}}{|}}{\overset{\overset{\text{CH}_3}{|}}{\text{C}}}\text{—CH}_2\text{—}\cdots \xrightarrow{\text{HI}} \cdots\text{—}\underset{\underset{\text{OH}}{|}}{\overset{\overset{\text{CH}_3}{|}}{\text{C}}}\text{—CH}_2\text{—}\cdots + \text{H}_2\text{O} + \text{I}_2
$$

The reaction of hydroperoxydated polypropylene with alkylaluminum compounds has also been studied. The oxidation of polypropylene fiber after treatment with $3-15\%$ solution of triethylaluminum in heptane for 5 minutes at room temperature yielded products not containing any hydroperoxy groups. These products displayed a band at $3,330$ cm^{-1} in their IR absorption spectra, which was attributed to the hydroxyl group. It is assumed /98/ that the conversion of the hydroperoxy to hydroxyl groups includes the formation of organometallic derivatives of the hydroperoxides and a rearrangement of the hydroperoxy salts of alkylaluminum to the hydroxy derivatives:

$$\underset{\substack{|\\ \text{OOH}}}{\overset{\substack{\text{CH}_3\\|}}{\cdots-\text{C}-\text{CH}_2-}}\cdots \xrightarrow{\text{AlR}_3} \underset{\substack{|\\ \text{O}-\text{O}-\text{Al}\big\langle{}^{R}_{R}}}{\overset{\substack{\text{CH}_3\\|}}{\cdots-\text{C}-\text{CH}_2-}}\cdots \xrightarrow{\text{Rearrangement}}$$

$$\rightarrow \underset{\substack{|\\ \text{OAl}\big\langle{}^{\text{OR}}_{R}}}{\overset{\substack{\text{CH}_3\\|}}{\cdots-\text{C}-\text{CH}_2-}}\cdots \xrightarrow{\text{Hydrolysis}} \underset{\substack{|\\ \text{OH}}}{\overset{\substack{\text{CH}_3\\|}}{\cdots-\text{C}-\text{CH}_2-}}\cdots$$

The conversion of the hydroperoxy to hydroxy groups reduces the tendency of polypropylene to undergo oxidation.

The hydroxylated polypropylene takes up azo dyes. Hydroxylation with the aim of increasing dye takeup is preferable in certain respects to graft polymerization performed for the same purpose. One of these advantages is that laborious identification of the grafting products becomes unnecessary.

Macromolecules containing hydroxyl groups in the chain may undergo various transformations in the chain.

Hydroxylated polypropylene can be cross-linked with the aid of diisocyanates /99/.

Oxidative degradation processes of polyolefins have been described. An important instance is polypropylene intended for the production of fibers, which was oxidized by hot air under pressure in alcohol and water suspensions and in solutions /32, 100/.

Advanced oxidative degradation of atactic /101/ and isotactic /102/ polypropylene yielded waxlike products. The degradation rate increased when the heating was conducted in the presence of a peroxide /103/, such as di-tert-butyl peroxide /101/.

Polypropylene is oxidized by ozone very vigorously, without a preliminary induction period /32/. The oxidation can also be performed by potassium bichromate, potassium permanganate dissolved in sulfuric acid /104/, nitric acid or nitrogen dioxide /105/. Various physical treatments of polypropylene in the presence of oxygen (ultrasonic degradation, electric arc, corona discharge) are also accompanied by oxidation /32/.

THERMAL DEGRADATION

In the absence of oxygen, polyethylene is very stable to heat /106, 107/. Heating polyethylene out of contact with oxygen does not produce degradation below 290°C /108, 109/. Further increase in the temperature results in a decrease in molecular weight. Above 360°C gaseous decomposition products are evolved, and complete decomposition of polyethylene takes place at about 475°C. The main degradation product is a waxlike substance /108/, the molecular weight of which remains constant at 692, irrespective of the conditions of pyrolysis (initial polyethylene had an average molecular weight of 20,000). Small amounts of low-boiling hydrocarbons and gases, mainly methane, are also evolved. Products of thermal decomposition of poly-ethylene contain practicall̦ no ethylene, unlike many other polymers (polystyrene, polyisobutylene, polyacrylates, etc.) which are degraded to the corresponding monomer.

Thermal degradation of polyethylene is satisfactorily described in terms of the mechanism proposed by Simha et al. /110 − 112/. The polymer chains are ruptured at the C−C bonds, with formation of free radicals (initiation):

$$
\cdots-\underset{\underset{H}{|}}{\overset{\overset{H}{|}}{C}}-\underset{\underset{H}{|}}{\overset{\overset{H}{|}}{C}}-\underset{\underset{H}{|}}{\overset{\overset{H}{|}}{C}}-\underset{\underset{H}{|}}{\overset{\overset{H}{|}}{C}}-\cdots \longrightarrow \cdots-\underset{\underset{H}{|}}{\overset{\overset{H}{|}}{C}}-\underset{\underset{H}{|}}{\overset{\overset{H}{|}}{C}}\bullet \;+\; \bullet\underset{\underset{H}{|}}{\overset{\overset{H}{|}}{C}}-\underset{\underset{H}{|}}{\overset{\overset{H}{|}}{C}}-\cdots
$$

The macroradicals may accept a hydrogen atom from another chain or from the same chain, with formation of a terminal double bond and of a new free radical (chain transfer):

$$
\cdots-\overset{H}{\underset{H}{C}}-\overset{H}{\underset{H}{C}}\bullet \;+\; \cdots-C-C-C-C+C-\cdots \longrightarrow
$$

$$
\longrightarrow \cdots-\overset{H}{\underset{H}{C}}-CH \;+\; \cdots-C-C-C=C \;+\; \bullet C-\cdots
$$

Chain termination is effected by recombination of two free radicals:

$$
2\cdots-\overset{H}{\underset{H}{C}}-\overset{H}{\underset{H}{C}}\bullet \longrightarrow \cdots-C-C-C-C-\cdots
$$

Degradation may also take place without any formation of free radicals /113, 114/. The C−C bonds may be broken as a result of stresses produced in the macromolecular chain by their thermal motion. If the number of hydrogen atoms is sufficiently large (unbranched chain), intramolecular hydrogen transfer to the place of bond cleavage may take place:

$$
\cdots-C-C-C+C-C-C-\cdots \longrightarrow \cdots-C-C=C \;+\; H-C-C-C-\cdots
$$

78

If some of the hydrogen atoms are substituted by, say, methyl groups, hydrogen transfer takes place only in some of the acts of chain cleavage, while in the remaining acts of chain cleavage free radicals are formed, by way of which the degradation is continued to the monomer stage. The formation of the monomer during the pyrolysis of polyisobutylene may be represented as follows /107/:

```
   CH3 H  CH3 ┊    H  CH3 H              CH3 H  CH3    CH3 H  CH3
    |  |   |  ┊    |   |  |               |  |   |      |  |   |
…—C—C—C—┊—C—C—C—…  ⟶  …—C—C—C•+ •C—C—C—…
    |  |   |  ┊    |   |  |               |  |   |      |  |   |
   CH3 H  CH3 ┊    H  CH3 H              CH3 H  CH3    CH3 H  H

              CH3 ┊  H  CH3                  CH3  H  CH3
               |  ┊  |   |                    |   |   |
            …—C—┊—C—C•   ⟶   …—C•  + C=C
               |  ┊  |   |                    |   |   |
              CH3 ┊  H  CH3                  CH3  H  CH3
```

In fact, up to 18% of the monomer are liberated in the thermal degradation of polyisobutylene.

The activation energy of thermal degradation increases with increasing molecular weight of the polymer. Thus, the activation energy of the thermal degradation of a polyethylene with a molecular weight of 11,000 was found to be 46 kcal/mole, while being 52.6 and 66.1 kcal/mole for polyethylenes with molecular weights of 16,000 and 23,000 respectively /115/. The degradation rate clearly decreases as the molecular weight of the initial polymer increases. It was shown by studying copolymers of ethylene with varying amounts of propylene /116/ that the degree of branching affects the rate of thermal degradation. As a number of the methyl branches increases, the degradation rate increases as well.

A reduction in the molecular weight of polyethylene and ethylene copolymers by thermal degradation is used to improve the flow properties and to prepare low-molecular, waxlike products /117—120/. For example, polyethylene or ethylene copolymer with a density of more than 0.94 g/cm^3 and with a molecular weight of more than 20,000 is heated out of contact with oxygen at 270—300°C for a time which is necessary to reduce the melt index by not less than 15%. The thermal treatment may be carried out simultaneously with the mechanical treatment, e.g., in a continuous action extruder /119/.

Polypropylene, in which every other carbon atom in the main chain is tertiary, is less resistant to the rupture of C—C bonds in the main chain than is polyethylene. During the thermal degradation of polypropylene, the cleavage of C—C bonds is usually accompanied by a transfer of a hydrogen atom:

```
   H  CH3 H ┊ CH3 H  CH3            H  CH3 H          CH3 H  CH3
   |   |  | ┊  |  |   |             |   |  |           |  |   |
…—C—C—C┊C—C—C—…  ⟶  …—C—C=C  +  H—C—C—C—…
   |   |  | ┊  |  |   |             |   |              |  |   |
   H  [H] H ┊ H  H   H             H   H             H  H   H
```

In fact, up to 18% of the monomer are liberated in the thermal degradation of polyisobutylene.

The process is favored by the larger mobility of the hydrogen atom at the tertiary carbon atom. Chain cleavage with formation of free radicals, their subsequent decomposition and formation of propylene is much less likely. This is shown by the insignificant amounts of propylene found in the products of thermal degradation of polypropylene /107/.

Thermal degradation of both polypropylene and polyethylene is employed in order to reduce their molecular weight /120, 123/. Thus, a more easily worked polypropylene is obtained if the polymer with a high molecular weight is heated up to 400°C in vacuo or in an inert gas medium /122/. The viscosity of the melt will also decrease if the action of heat is accompanied by effect of mechanical vibrations, such as may be produced by ultrasonics /123/.

Bibliography

1. Jones, G.— In: Chemical Reactions of Polymers (edited by E. Fettes).— New York, Wiley. 1964.
2. British Patent 481515. 1938.
3. US Patent 2849431. 1958.
4. US Patent 2389803. 1946.
5. US Patent 2422919. 1947.
6. US Patent 2481188. 1949.
7. Krentsel, B. A., D. E. Il'ina, and S. A. Adylov. — Plast. Massy, No. 6: 3. 1963.
8. US Patent 2405971. 1946.
9. US Patent 2503252. 1950.
10. Michail, R., F. Gherghel, M. Stanescu, and S. Kornbaum. — Rev. chim., 12 (5): 275. 1961.
11. Smook, M. A., W. J. Remington, and D. E. Strain. — In: Polythene. The Technology and Uses of Ethylene Polymers (edited by A. Renfrew and P. Morgan).— New York, Interscience. 1960.
12. French Patent 1324506. 1962.
13. French Patent 1320413. 1963.
14. US Patent 2571901. 1951.
15. Canadian Patent 471037. 1951.
16. Myers, C. S. — Ind. Eng. Chem., 44: 1095. 1952.
17. US Patent 2183556. 1940.
18. US Patent 2926159. 1960.
19. US Patent 2592763. 1952.
20. Thompson, H. W. and P. Torkington. — Trans. Faraday Soc., 41: 246. 1945.
21. Thompson, H. W. and P. Torkington. — Proc. Roy. Soc., 184A: 2. 1945.
22. Oakes, W. G. and R. B. Richards. — Trans. Faraday Soc., 42A: 197. 1946.
23. Smook, M. A., F. T. Pieski, and C. F. Hammer. — Ind. Eng. Chem., 45: 2731. 1953.
24. Adylov, S. A., I. F. Leshcheva, D. E. Il'ina, M. V. Shishkina, and B. A. Krentsel'. — Neftekhimiya, 3 (1): 82. 1963.
25. Brooks, R. E., D. E. Strain, and A. McAlevy. — India Rubber World, 127: 791. 1953.

26. US Patent 2541492. 1951.
27. A d y l o v, S. A. — Author's Summary of Candidate's Thesis, Moskva. 1963.
28. A d y l o v, S. A., D. E. I l ' i n a, B. A. K r e n t s e l ', and M. V. S h i s h k i n a. — Vysokomolekulyarnye Soedineniya, 5 (3): 316. 1963.
29. US Patent 2497046. 1950.
30. US Patent 2811468. 1958.
31. British Patent 710523. 1954.
32. M a n á s e k, Z. and D. B e l l u s. Polipropilen (Polypropylene), p. 126, edited by V. I. Pilipovskii and I. K. Yartsev. — Izdatel'stvo "Khimiya." 1967.
33. M i n s k e r, K. S. and V. S. E t l i s. — Doklady AN SSSR, 123 (6): 1041. 1958.
34. K r e n t s e l ', B. A., A. V. T o p c h i e v, and D. E. I l ' i n a. — ZhPKh, 32 (6): 1404. 1959.
35. British Patent 843209. 1960.
36. British Patent 811848. 1959.
37. C a m p b e l l, T. W. and D. J. L y m a n. — J. Polymer Sci., 55: 169. 1961.
38. British Patent 834905. 1960.
39. C a m p b e l l, T. W. and A. C. H a v e n. — J. Appl. Polymer Sci., 1: 78. 1959.
40. K a m b a r a, S h u and T a k a o O h s h i k a.—Koguo Kagaku Zasshi, 62: 1781. 1959; Chem. Abstr., 57: 13959. 1962.
41. Italian Patent 591501. 1958.
42. K a m b a r a, S h u and T a k a o O h s h i k a. — J. Chem. Soc. Japan, Ind. Chem. Soc., 62 (1)): 1781. 1959.
43. British Patent 877880. 1961.
44. K a w a i, W a s a b u r o, S h i g e r u T s u t s u m i.—Nippon Kagaku Zasshi, 80: 780. 1959; Chem. Abstr., 55: 3410. 1961.
45. K r e n t s e l ', B. A., G. E. S e m e n i d o, and D. E. I l ' i n a.—Vysoko-molekulyarnye Soedineniya, 5 (4): 558. 1963.
46. K r e n t s e l ', B. A., G. E. S e m e n i d o, D. E. I l ' i n a, and M. V. S h i s h k i n a. — Vysokomolekulyarnye Soedineniya, 5 (4): 564. 1963.
47. M i k h a i l o v, N. V., L. G. T o k a r e v a, and V. S. K l i m e n k o v. — Kolloidnyi Zhurnal, 18: 578. 1956.
48. A r l m a n n, E. G. — J. Polymer Sci., 12 (67): 543, 547. 1954.
49. US Patent 2906743. 1960.
50. Italian Patent 537429. 1955.
51. Austrian Patent 210135. 1960.
52. V i s s e r, P. J. — Plastica, 15: 282. 1962.
53. Japanese Patent 15277. 1961.
54. British Patent 868158. 1961.
55. Italian Patent 597560. 1959.
56. Y a k u b o v i c h, A. Ya. and Yu. M. Z i n o v ' e v. — Uspekhi Khimii, 17 (5): 581. 1947.
57. G i l b e r t, E. E. and E. P. J o n e s. — Ind. Eng. Chem., 43 (9): 2028. 1951.
58. G i l b e r t, E. E. and E. P. J o n e s. — Ind. Eng. Chem., 46 (9): 1895. 1954.
59. US Patent 2640048. 1953.
60. US Patent 2416061. 1947.

61. US Patent 2586363. 1952.
62. Schumacher, H.J. and J. Stanff. — J. Chim., 55: 341. 1942.
63. British Patent 815234. 1959.
64. GFR Patent 970578. 1958.
65. US Patent 2889259. 1959.
66. US Patent 2556879. 1951.
67. US Patent 2658883. 1953.
68. US Patent 2578904. 1951.
69. Warner, R.R. — Rubber Age, 71: 205. 1952.
70. Catton, N.H. — Kautschuk Gummi, 9(11); 280. 1956.
71. Salomon, G., C. Konigsberger, and A. Ultee. — J. Rubber
    Techn. Cont. Proc., 106. 1948.
72. Salomon, G., and C. Konigsberger. — J. Rec. trav. chim.,
    69: 711. 1950; 70: 545. 1951.
73. Salomon, G. and A. Ultee. — J. Rec. trav. chim., 69:95. 1950;
    70: 537. 1951.
74. Nersasian, A. and D. Andersen. — Proceedings of Intern.
    Rubber Conference, p. 537, Washington. 1959.
75. Nersasian, A. and D.E. Anderson. — J. Appl. Polymer Sci.,
    4: 74. 1960.
76. Il'ina, D.E., B.A. Krentsel', and A.V. Topchiev. — Vysoko-
    molekulyarnye Soedineniya, 3: 995. 1961.
77. US Patent 2972604. 1961.
78. US Patent 3050503. 1962.
79. Sobue, H., Y. Tajima, and Y. Tabata. — Koguo Kagaku Zasshi,
    62: 1774. 1959; Chem. Abstr., 57: 15332. 1962.
80. Ohshika, T. — Koguo Kagaku Zasshi, 64(7):1299. 1961.
81. Italian Patent 591501. 1958.
82. Soviet Patent 149773. 1962; Byulleten' Izobretatelya, No. 17. 1962.
83. Schroeder, J.P. and W.P. Sopchak. — J. Polymer Sci., 47:
    417. 1960.
84. US Patent 3008939. 1961.
85. Bellus, D., Z. Manásek, and M. Lazar. — Vysokomolekulyarnye
    Soedineniya, 5: 145. 1963.
86. British Patent 849058. 1960.
87. Manásek, Z., D. Bellus, and B. Böhmer. — Chem. zvesti,
    17: 318. 1963.
88. Leonard, E.C., W.E. Loed, J.H. Mason, and W.L. Wheel-
    wright. — J. Appl. Polymer·Sci., 5: 157. 1961.
89. Leonard, E.C., W.E. Loed, J.H. Mason, and J.A. Stenstrom. —
    J. Polymer Sci., 55: 799. 1961.
90. Haywood, C.K. — In: Polythene. The Technology and Uses of Ethylene
    Polymers (edited by A. Renfrew and P. Morgan). — New York,
    Interscience. 2nd ed. 1960.
91. Gordon, G. Ya. Stabilizatsiya sinteticheskikh polimerov (Stabilization
    of Synthetic Polymers), p. 175. — Goskhimizdat. 1963.
92. Rugg, F.M., J.J. Smith, and R.C. Bacon. — J. Polymer Sci.,
    13: 535. 1954.
93. Grafmüller, F. and F. Husemann. — Makromol. Chem.,
    40 (161): 172. 1960.
94. Pross, A.V. and R.M. Black. — J. Soc. Chem. Ind., 69: 113. 1950.
95. Hawkins, W.L., W. Matreyek, and F.H. Winslow. — J. Polymer
    Sci., 41: 1. 1959.

96. British Patent 581279. 1946.
97. Natta, G., E. Beati, and F. Severini. — J. Polymer Sci.,
    34: 685. 1959.
98. Minsker, K. S., I. Z. Shapiro, and G. A. Razuvaev. —
    Vysokomolekulyarnye Soedineniya, 4 (3): 351. 1962.
99. British Patent 832068. 1960.
100. British Patent 910040. 1962.
101. US Patent 2828296. 1958.
102. US Patent 2911384. 1959.
103. Freund, L. and L. Ambrose. Polipropilen (Polypropylene),
    p. 198, edited by V. I. Pilipovskii and I. K. Yartsev. — Izdatel'stvo
    "Khimiya." 1967.
104. Belgian Patent 569129. 1958.
105. US Patent 2987501. 1961.
106. Schwartz, A. and G. Cramer. — In: Polythene. The Technology
    and Uses of Ethylene Polymers (edited by A. Renfrew and
    P. Morgan). — New York, Interscience, 2nd ed. 1960.
107. Madorsky, S. Termicheskoe razlozhenie organicheskikh polimerov
    (Thermal Decomposition of Organic Polymers), p. 103. —
    Izdatel'stvo "Mir." 1967.
108. Madorsky, S. L., S. Straus, D. Thompson, and
    S. Williamson. — J. Polymer Sci., 4:639. 1949.
109. Oakes, W. G. and R. B. Richards. — J. Chem. Soc., 2929. 1949.
110. Simha, R., L. A. Wall, and P. J. Blatz. — J. Polymer Sci.,
    5: 615. 1950.
111. Simha, R. and L. A. Wall. — J. Phys. Chem., 56: 707. 1952.
112. Simha, R., L. A. Wall, and J. Bram. — J. Chem. Phys., 29: 894.
    1958.
113. Madorsky, S. L. and S. Straus. — J. Res. Nat. Bur. Stand., 53:
    361. 1954.
114. Madorsky, S. L. — Soc. Plastics Eng. J., 17: 665. 1961.
115. Jellinek, H. H. G. — J. Polymer Sci., 4: 13. 1949.
116. Wall, L. A. and S. Straus. — J. Polymer Sci., 44: 313. 1960.
117. US Patent 2372001. 1942.
118. British Patent 569043. 1945.
119. British Patent 1000911. 1965.
120. US Patent 3230288. 1966.
121. Wisseroth, K. — Angew. Chem., 72(22):866. 1960.
122. Japanese Patent 15807. 1965.
123. Japanese Patent 1654. 1965.

Chapter V

POLYOLEFINS WITH A TRIDIMENSIONAL STRUCTURE

The preparation of polyolefins with a tridimensional structure is an important technique for their modification. Cross-linking results in a considerable improvement of important parameters such as resistance to heat, tensile strength, resistance to cracking, resistance to the action of solvents, etc. Cross-linking may be effected by way of specially introduced functional groups, radiation-chemical and photochemical effects and cross-linking agents, mainly of the peroxide type.

PREPARATION OF TRIDIMENSIONAL STRUCTURES
BY INTRODUCTION OF FUNCTIONAL GROUPS

After functional groups have been introduced into the molecule of polyethylene, polypropylene, ethylene-propylene copolymers or copolymers of ethylene with other α-olefins by sulfochlorination, halogenation or phosphorylation, various reagents are added in order to effect cross-linking. Thus, the cross-linking (vulcanization) of sulfochlorinated polyethylene — which has been studied in most detail, owing to its industrial importance — may be effected by reacting the sulfonyl chloride groups with metal oxides to yield salts, or else with diamines when sulfamide groups are obtained /1, 2/. Cross-links are also formed by reaction between diamines and chlorine atoms located in β-position to sulfonyl chloride groups on tertiary carbon atoms. Owing to the formation of double bonds by the splitting of hydrogen chloride and sulfur dioxide off the sulfochlorinated polyethylene under the action of heat, it is possible to cross-link polyethylene by sulfur in the presence of accelerators used in the vulcanization of rubbers.

The main industrial technique is the cross-linking of sulfochlorinated polyethylene (chlorine content 25 − 40%) with the aid of oxides of bivalent and polyvalent metals (magnesium, lead, etc.) /3, 4/. Cross-linking with metal oxides is effected at 125 − 160°C, and is feasible only in the presence of moisture. It is believed that the sulfonyl chloride groups are hydrolyzed, after which intermolecular cross-links are formed /5/:

$$RSO_2Cl + H_2O \longrightarrow HCl + RSO_2OH$$

$$MeO + 2HCl \longrightarrow MeCl_2 + H_2O$$

$$MeO + 2RSO_2OH \longrightarrow RSO_2O—Me—OSO_2R + H_2O$$

84

The cross-linked products, unlike polyethylene itself, are highly resistant to the action of ozone, oxygen, nitric and chromic acids and other oxidizing agents. The sum total of the mechanical properties of the cross-linked sulfochlorinated polyethylene is similar to that of vulcanized synthetic rubbers. However, cross-linked sulfochlorinated polyethylene is harder, has a higher tensile strength and elasticity modulus, is much more resistant to cracking and to abrasion and has a smaller elongation.

A comparison of the properties of cross-linked materials obtained from polymers with differing crystallinities shows that it is preferable to sulfochlorinate polymers which are relatively amorphous. Thus, for instance, the products of cross-linking of an amorphous sulfochlorinated ethylene-propylene copolymer, containing 20 wt. % chlorine (I) have the same or superior parameters as those of cross-linked sulfochlorinated high-pressure polyethylene containing 30 wt. % chlorine (II) /6, 7/:

Properties of cross-linked sulfochlorinated high-pressure polyethylene and ethylene-propylene copolymer

	I	II
Tensile strength, kg/cm^2	90—125	100—130
Elongation, %	300—400	350—400
Modulus at 100% elongation, kg/cm^2	10—15	12—15
Shore hardness A	50—60	60—65
Residual elongation, %	10	20—30
Elasticity, %	35—45	25

Since the amorphization of polypropylene as a result of sulfochlorination is very advanced, the chlorine contents required for the preparation of cross-linked elastomers are much lower for polypropylene than for poly-ethylene.

The best procedure is to use sulfochlorinated polypropylene containing up to 20% chlorine, with up to 10% crystallinity and a molecular weight above 5,000 /8/. As in the cross-linking of sulfochlorinated polyethylene, the product which has been cross-linked by metal oxides can only be prepared in the presence of water. The amount of the metal oxide is usually 10 – 40 wt. %. The cross-linking temperature is 150 – 170°C. Thiourea and diamines can be used as cross-linking agents in lieu of metal oxides /9/.

The products of cross-linking of sulfochlorinated polypropylene display highly reversible deformation, high elasticity, mechanical strength and resistance to the action of ozone /8/.

The hydrolyzed products of chlorophosphorylation $(-\overset{\displaystyle |}{\underset{\displaystyle |}{C}}-POCl_2)$ which contain phosphonic groups $-PO(OH)_2$ are also capable of being cross-linked by metal oxides (lead, zinc, etc. oxides) /10, 11/. The content of phosphorus in the phosphorylated ethylene-propylene copolymer (90% propylene links) at which it is possible to cross-link with zinc oxide is about 1% /12/. The cross-linked material based on phosphorylated poly-propylene /13/ is distinguished by a high resistance to the action of ozone; if the phosphorus content is about 5%, it becomes self-quenching /8/.

Chlorinated polypropylene can be cross-linked /14 − 17/ by zinc, lead and magnesium oxides. The resulting cross-linked elastomers are highly resistant to the action of ozone. Materials cross-linked with diamines display a high mechanical strength /18/.

Unsaturated groups in ternary copolymers of ethylene with propylene and another diene (Chapter II) make it possible to cross-link these products in a manner similar to that employed in the sulfur vulcanization of rubbers /19, 20/. Ternary copolymers can also be cross-linked by reaction with dibenzoylquinonedioxime in the presence of lead oxide. The vulcanizate is more resistant to aging than the product cross-linked with sulfur. A highly heat-resistant and elastic elastomer can be obtained if phenol-formaldehyde resins are employed as cross-linking agents. These resins are prepared from p-octylphenol, tert-butylphenol and p,p'-dihydroxydiphenylpropane as the phenolic constituent.

Polyolefins may also be rendered capable of being cross-linked by the introduction of functional groups into the molecule. Thus, for instance, carboxylated polymers, prepared by copolymerization of ethylene with acrylic or methacrylic acid, can be cross-linked, similarly to carboxylated rubbers /21 − 23/, by oxides and salts of polyvalent metals.

A recent development are materials with tridimensional structure − the so-called ionomers, which are prepared from copolymers of α-olefins (ethylene, propylene, α-butylene, etc.) with unsaturated monocarboxylic or dicarboxylic acids by neutralization of some of the carboxyl groups by salts or hydroxides of metals (Li, K, Na, Mg, Sr, Zn, Cu, Pb, etc.) /24 − 27/. The content of carboxylated links in the ionomers does not exceed 25 mole %. Not less than 10% of carboxyl hydrogens are substituted by metal ions, preferably ions of an alkali or an alkaline earth metal. Optimum properties of ionomers are attained when 50 − 80% of the carboxyl groups have been neutralized.

Carboxylated polyolefins include both products of copolymerization of olefins with unsaturated acids and products of saponification of copolymers of olefins with unsaturated acid esters, as well as products of grafting unsaturated acids to the polyolefin.

Owing to the ionic nature of the cross-links, these materials display a number of typical properties. The most important one is that the cross-linking of ionomers is reversible. An elevated working temperature results in the rupture of most of the ionic cross-links and the material behaves as a thermoplastic resin. After cooling, the ionic links are restored and the material again acquires a tridimensional structure.

Ionomers display a combination of very valuable properties. They have a high tensile strength and elongation at break; they are stable to solvents and oils; they do not crack under the action of externally applied stresses; they are arc-resistant; they adhere better than polyethylene to various materials and display improved dye takeup. The properties of one such ionomer are listed below:

Properties of the ionomer Surlyn A /28, 29/

Density, g/cm³	0.93—0.96
Melt index at 190°C, g/10 min	0.1—4.0
Tensile strength, kg/cm²	245—390
Tensile impact strength, kg·cm/cm³	124—330
Elongation at break, %	300—400
Elasticity modulus, kg/cm²	1,900—2,800
Izod impact strength, kg·cm/cm²	30—77
Vicat softening point, °C	71—96
Maximum working temperature, °C	330
Service temperature range not under load, °C	−118 to +88°C
Dielectric loss factor at 10³ sec⁻¹	0.0015
Dielectric constant at 10³ sec⁻¹	2.5
Electric volume resistivity, ohm·cm	$0.5 \cdot 10^{17}$
Dielectric strength, kV/mm	40

Ionomers with different structures and properties can be prepared by varying the content of carboxyl groups, and the number and the identity of the metal ions. The presence of ionic bonds in copolymers with a low content of carboxyl groups (up to 1 mole %) does not significantly affect their crystallinity /26/. When the acid content is increased to 7 − 10 mole %, advanced amorphization of the copolymer takes place, and the ionization of the carboxyl group then affects the nature of crystalline formations to a smaller extent.

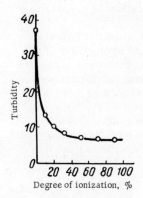

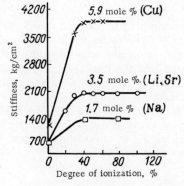

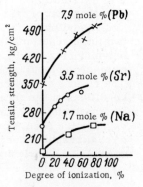

FIGURE 52. Turbidity of co-polymers as a function of their degree of ionization (content of monocarboxylic acid, 3.5 mole %; cation, sodium) /26/.

FIGURE 53. Stiffness of ionomers as a function of their degree of ionization at varying contents of monocarboxylic acid /26/.

FIGURE 54. Tensile strength of ionomers as a function of their degree of ionization for various contents of mono-carboxylic acid /26/.

The amorphization of the structure by the effect of ionogenic groups is reflected in the transparency of the ionomers. This effect is due to the absence of light scattering by crystalline structures, which is noted in conventional polyolefins. Figure 52 shows the decrease in the turbidity of the ionomer with increasing degree of ionization. Despite their amorphous structure, ionomers have a considerable stiffness, owing to the presence of hydrogen bonds between the carboxyl groups. The stiffness obviously increases with increasing acid content, but past a given degree of ionization the stiffness does not increase any further (Figure 53). The tensile strength increases with increasing content of carboxyl groups and their degree of ionization (Figure 54), but the relative elongation at break decreases.

PREPARATION OF POLYMERS WITH TRIDIMENSIONAL STRUCTURE BY RADIATION-CHEMICAL AND PHOTOCHEMICAL METHODS

Radiation-chemical cross-linking. Extensive literature, in particular a number of reviews /30 — 34/, deal with radiation-chemical cross-linking and with the structure and properties of cross-linked polyolefins (chiefly polyethylene).

In industry, cross-linking of polyolefins is best carried out by β- and γ-radiation. If fast electrons are used (β-radiation), the cross-linking may be effected more efficiently, since high-energy electrons may be produced in electron accelerators. However, the penetrating power of fast electrons is relatively small. If the electron energy is 2 MeV, the substrate material is uniformly affected to an approximate depth of 1 cm. Materials used in the manufacture of thick-walled vessels may be cross-linked with Co^{60} γ-radiation, even though the intensity of this radiation is usually much less than that of fast electrons.

Cross-linking is accompanied by degradation. The relative rates of these two main reactions largely determine the structure and properties of the polymer obtained by irradiation and will depend on the chemical structure of macromolecular chains and the nature of supermolecular formations. The results of the irradiation also depend to a considerable extent on the conditions of the irradiation.

In polyethylene, cross-linking is typically the main reaction, while degradation occurs only to a minor extent. The number of elementary acts of chain rupture corresponding to one elementary cross-linking act β/α is given by Charlesby's equation /31/:

$$\beta/a = s + \sqrt{s}$$

where s is the content of the sol fraction, equal to $1 - g$; g is the content of the insoluble gel fraction (ratio between the weight of the insoluble residue from the extraction of the specimen with a hot solvent, say, xylene, and the weight of the specimen prior to the extraction).

If degradation and cross-linking processes take place at the same time and the latter process predominates, the magnitude of s will tend to a limit with increasing radiation dose (r) The value of this limit will depend on the relative rates of the two processes and will not be zero, unless the degradation rate can be neglected in comparison with the rate of cross-linking. If we extrapolate $(s + \sqrt{s}) = f(1/r)$ to zero, we can find β/α at $r \to \infty$. This value is $0.18 - 0.20$ for polyethylene /35/. It is interesting to note that the degradation of high-pressure polyethylene by irradiation yields six times more low-molecular hydrocarbon products than does a similar degradation of low-pressure polyethylene /36/. The exact reason for this difference is not known, but it may be assumed that it is connected with the instability of the chain fragments with tertiary carbon atoms under irradiation.

The β/α ratios found for ethylene — propylene copolymer (7 mole % of propylene) and ethylene — α-butylene copolymer (3 mole % of α-butylene), cross-linked with fast electrons, were, respectively, 0.24 ± 0.03 and 0.14 ± 0.03 /37, 38/, which is close to the value obtained for polyethylene.

In radiation-chemical cross-linking of polypropylene the degradation of the main chains proceeds at a rate which is of the same order as the rate of cross-linking, viz., $\beta/\alpha \approx 0.75 - 1.0$ /39 — 41/.

Data on the relationship between the behavior of a polymer on being irradiated and its position in the series of products of polymerization of higher α-olefins are not available. It is known, however, that polypentene-1 and polyhexene-1 are cross-linked when irradiated /42/. It has been shown, by studying the content of the sol fraction as a function of the fast electron irradiation dose, that gel-fraction can be detected in samples of polypentene when the radiation dose has attained about 24 Mrad, while for polyhexene this magnitude is about 7 Mrad. When the dose was insufficient for the formation of the gel fraction, a marked decrease in the molecular weight was observed.

A study of EPR spectra of irradiated polybutene-1 and polypentene-1 revealed the presence of free radicals formed as a result of the rupture of C—H bonds both in the main chain and in the side chains /43/. The rupture of the side chains with formation of vinylene groups is probably connected with the presence of lone electrons on branched carbon atoms:

$$
\begin{array}{ccc}
\overset{\bullet}{C}H_2 & & \\
| & & \\
CH_2 & & \overset{\bullet}{C}H \\
| & & \| \\
\cdots-CH_2-CH-CH_2-\cdots & \longrightarrow \quad CH_4 + & \cdots-CH_2-C-CH_2-\cdots
\end{array}
$$

The main reaction produced by the irradiation of polyisobutylene is degradation /44, 45/. It is assumed that one reason for the radiation instability of polyisobutylene is the low energy of C—C bonds in the main chain, owing to the steric strains produced by methyl groups.

The connection between the effect of radiation-chemical cross-linking and the crystallinity is an important problem, which mainly concerns the industrial modification of polyolefins by the radiation-chemical method. The data on this subject are contradictory. Charlesby et al. and other workers /31, 34, 46 — 50/ determined the swelling and the elasticity modulus of irradiated specimens of high density and low-density poly- ethylene and concluded that the rates of the cross-linking process were the same in crystalline and in amorphous regions. Lawton et al. /51, 52/, on the contrary, studied the cross-linking of polyethylene during irradiation with fast electrons above the melting temperatures of crystalline regions and concluded that the cross-linking process takes place exclusively in the amorphous regions. The low degree of cross-linking in crystalline regions is connected with the low mobility of free macroradicals /51 — 53/.

Studies of the variation in the crystallinity and in the size of the crystallites during irradiation also indicate that the cross-linking rate is faster in the amorphous regions /54/. The preferential cross-linking in amorphous regions has not yet been conclusively demonstrated, but the opposite point of view, according to which the cross-linking proceeds at similar rates in crystalline and in amorphous regions, can no longer be admitted /34/.

Comparative studies of the cross-linking effects produced by fast electrons in substrates with differing degrees of crystallinity and degrees of branching confirm that cross-linking preferentially takes place in amorphous regions /55/. The cross-linking effect was estimated by measuring the elasticity modulus and the weight coefficient of swelling, which are known /46/ to be determined mainly by the distance between the cross-links and to be independent of the molecular weight. The dependence between the weight coefficient of swelling and crystallinity (Figure 55) shows that if the irradiation dose is small (10 and 20 Mrad), the cross-linking effect is stronger in less crystalline polyolefins. If the dose is increased to 100 Mrad, this relationship is no longer noted. The values of elasticity modulus, calculated by Hess' formula from the data of thermomechanical tests performed above the melting point of the crystals, are a function of the crystallinity of the irradiated polymers /38, 55/.

The results in Figure 56 also show that the cross-linking is more intensive in less crystalline polymers.

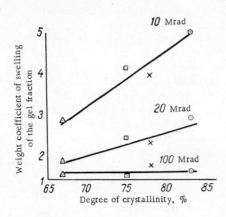

FIGURE 55. Weight coefficient of swelling in o-xylene at 120°C of the gel fraction of irradiated polyolefins as a function of crystallinity for different absorbed doses /55/:

Δ — copolymer of ethylene with α-butylene;
□ — copolymer of ethylene with propylene;
×, O — high-pressure polyethylene.

The magnitude of the dose affects the degree of cross-linking. The irradiation intensity determines the rate of formation of free radicals and thus also the rate of cross-linking. The radiation energy determines its depth of penetration. If low-energy radiation is employed, it is possible to modify the surface layer of the polymer only. Under otherwise identical conditions the type of radiation does not influence the effect of the irradiation to any great extent /33/.

The result of the irradiation largely depends on the medium in which it is effected.

Irradiation in the air (see Chapter III on the synthesis of graft copolymers) results in the oxidation of the polymer, mainly in the surface layers and in the amorphous regions in which it is easier for the oxygen to diffuse. Oxygen inhibits cross-linking by reacting with the intermediate compounds. The higher the content of hydroperoxide and carbonyl groups in polyethylene, the smaller the number of cross-links and of trans-vinylene groups /56/.

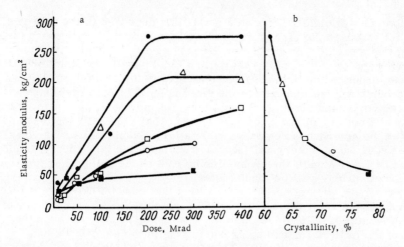

FIGURE 56. Elasticity modulus of polyolefins at 150°C as a function of the absorbed dose (a) and of crystallinity for a dose of 200 Mrad (b) /55/:

● — copolymer of ethylene with α-butylene, 61% crystalline; △ — copolymer of ethylene with propylene, 63% crystalline; □ — copolymer of ethylene with α-butylene, 67% crystalline; O — copolymer of ethylene with propylene, 72% crystalline; ■ — low-pressure polyethylene, 78% crystalline.

An important parameter of the irradiation process is the temperature /46, 53, 57/. The cross-linking rate increases with the temperature (Figure 57), probably owing to the increased mobility of the macroradicals. It may be expected that the degradation rate will not increase with the temperature to the same extent, since the mobility of polymer chains is not a relevant factor in the degradation reactions.

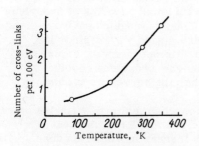

FIGURE 57. Number of cross-links in polyethylene produced by γ-radiation as a function of the temperature /57/.

If the irradiation temperature is varied, different cross-linked products may be obtained. Thus, for instance, the irradiation of polyethylene above its melting point yields a rubberlike material /58/. Irradiation at elevated temperatures may also be employed in the manufacture of transparent polyethylene articles /59—61/.

Ushakov et al. /62/ studied the melting temperatures and crystallinities of low-pressure polyethylene which had been irradiated at different temperatures and concluded that the nature of the lattice depended on the state of aggregation of the material during cross-linking. If molten polyethylene is irradiated, the random distribution of the chains is made permanent by cross-linking; the crystallinity and the melting temperature decrease. Cross-linking below the melting temperature is also accompanied by destruction of the crystalline formations in the vicinity of the cross-links.

If the dose is sufficiently large, the result is a decrease in the degree of crystallinity and in the size of crystalline regions and a decrease in the melting temperature. According to Ushakov et al. /62/, irradiation at low temperatures specifically results in a fixed parallel orientation of the chain, produced by the cross-links formed in the crystalline regions. This accounts for the increase in the melting point of the crystallites which remain behind after the irradiation. We may note that these interesting data are not in contradiction with the fact that cross-linking takes place mainly in the amorphous regions. While a large number of cross-links may be produced in the crystalline phase owing to the large doses employed /62/ (150 – 1,625 Mrad), the cross-linking rate in the amorphous fraction of the material may still be much faster.

Nevertheless, the statement to the effect that cross-linking takes place preferentially in amorphous regions /55/, which is based on the study of the spatial lattice, fails to take into account the difference between the nature of the lattices formed by cross-linking in the amorphous and crystalline phases respectively. This difference, which was noted by Ushakov et al. /62/, means that the contribution of each type of lattice to the properties of the cross-linked polymer (swelling coefficient and elasticity modulus above the melting point) is different. If the individual effects of each type of lattice could be determined, the differences between the cross-linking rates of amorphous and crystalline regions would be more accurately known.

The main parameter which is different in irradiated articles made of polyethylene and in those made of copolymers of ethylene with propylene and other α-olefins is their greater resistance to heat. The spatial structure imparts residual strength to the material, and the shape of the article is retained at temperatures above the melting point. Irradiated articles made of polyethylene, and copolymers of ethylene with small amounts of propylene or α-butylene can be utilized up to 150 – 200°C, unless under heavy mechanical loads. Thermomechanical tests are a good way to study the behavior of cross-linked polyolefins at elevated temperatures. Figure 58 shows the thermomechanical curves of an ethylene-propylene copolymer, before and after irradiation with fast electrons; the curves were obtained by the sphere indentation method /63/.

Samoilov /64/ studied the effect of radiation-chemical cross-linking on the thermophysical properties of polyethylene and found that the heat capacity and heat conductivity decreased with increasing radiation dose (Table 13).

TABLE 13. Change in the thermophysical properties of high-pressure polyethylene due to exposure to γ-radiation /64/

Parameter	Initial poly-ethylene	Irradiated polyethylene		
		81.3 Mrad	382.5 Mrad	610 Mrad
Thermal conductivity, W/m·°C · · ·	0.485	0.478	0.438	0.408
Thermal diffusivity · 10^6, m^2/sec · · ·	0.278	0.278	0.279	0.280
Specific heat, J/kg·°C · · · · · · · ·	1910	1800	1585	1450
Density, kg/m^3 · · · · · · · · · · ·	915	957	991	1005
Vicat softening point, °C · · · · · · ·	105	111	125	133

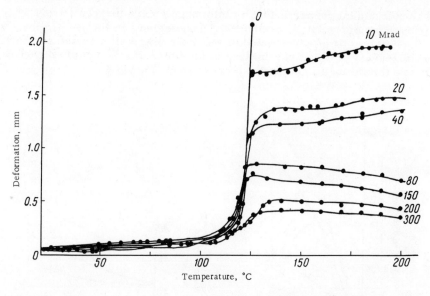

FIGURE 58.   Thermomechanical curves of the copolymer of ethylene with 7% propylene at various absorbed doses /38/

The decrease in the heat conductivity is due to the additional scattering and absorption of phonons on the cross-links between the main chains of the irradiated polyethylene. The cross-linking of macromolecular chains decreases the number of internal degrees of freedom, which in turn results in a decrease of the specific heat of polyethylene with increasing radiation dose. The changes in the physical and mechanical properties as a result of the irradiation are a reflection of the complexity of the transformations which occur in the polymer. Processes of cross-linking and degradation, disruption of crystalline structures and formation of relatively low-molecular degradation products all affect in different ways the behavior of the material subjected to deformation. The cross-linking reduces the mobility of the chain segments. Degradation and amorphization of the polymer has the opposite effect. As a result, the effect of radiation on the tensile strength, elongation at break and elasticity modulus of the polymer has an optimum which corresponds to definite radiation doses.

Irradiation of polyethylene with relatively small doses (a few dozen Mrad) does not materially affect the elasticity modulus. The crystallinity decreases with increasing dose. The effect of decreased crystallinity is not as strong as that of increased degree of cross-linking. The elasticity modulus tends to a minimum, which corresponds to doses producing advanced amorphization (about 500 — 600 Mrad). As the degree of cross-linking subsequently increases with increasing dose, the elasticity modulus shows a sharp rise /31/.

Curves showing the relationship between the tensile strength or relative elongation and the absorbed dose may show maxima at doses of the order of a few tens of Mrad.

The mechanical properties of irradiated polymers largely depend on the properties of the initial products. Thus, changes in the yield point and tensile strength are a function of the molecular weight of the starting material (Figure 59). The parameter values of the material are preserved if these are irradiated in an oxygen-free medium (Figure 60).

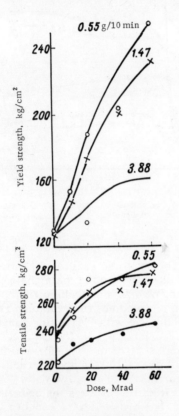

FIGURE 59. Mechanical properties of low-pressure polyethylene as a function of the absorbed dose at different values of the melt index of the initial material /65/.

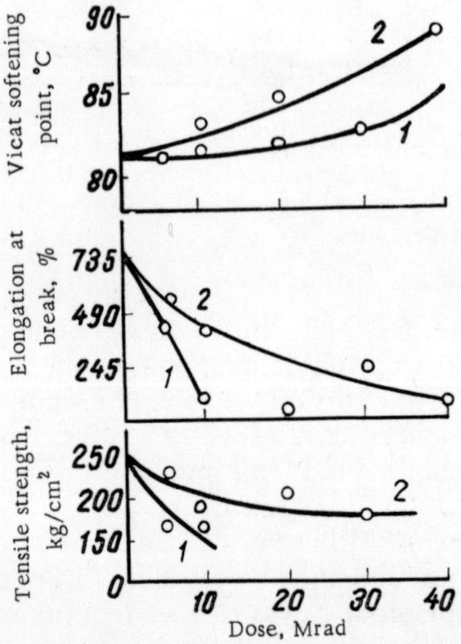

FIGURE 60. Mechanical properties of high-pressure polyethylene irradiated in the air (1) and in vacuo (2) as a function of the absorbed dose. Co[60] radiation /66/.

A similar description of the changes in the physicomechanical parameters of polyethylene under the action of ionizing radiation was also given by Charlesby /31/.

Another very important parameter is the increased resistance of polyethylene to cracking, resulting from radiation-chemical cross-linking /65, 67 — 69/. A marked increase in the resistance to cracking under prolonged loads, internal stresses, the action of surfactants, and other factors is attained even when small (10 — 20 Mrad) doses are absorbed. The higher the molecular weight of the polymer, the lower the absorbed dose which is required to produce a marked improvement in the resistance to cracking (Table 14).

TABLE 14. Effect of the absorbed dose on the resistance of low-pressure polyethylene to cracking /65/. Irradiation with 2.0 MeV electrons in an inert gas medium.* Dose rate 0.4 Mrad/min

Flow index of melt, g/10 min	Absorbed dose, Mrad	Resistance to cracking, hours*	
		in 20% solution of OP-7 at 50°C	in 20% solution of OP-10 at 80°C
3.88	0	90	1.5
	10	180	3.0
	20	>6,000	>4,000
	40	>6,000	>4,000
	60	>6,000	>4,000
1.47	0	120	3.0
	10	5,500	28
	20	>6,000	865
	40	>6,000	>4,000
	60	>6,000	>4,000
0.55	0	570	7.0
	10	3,000	840
	20	>6,000	1,180
	40	>6,000	>4,000
	60	>6,000	>4,000
0.16	0	1,200	25
	10	>6,000	3,000
	20	>6,000	2,500
	40	>6,000	>4,000
	60	>6,000	>4,000

* Resistance to cracking was defined as the time required for the failure of 50% of samples held under stress in aqueous surfactant solutions at the given temperature.

Irradiated polyethylene and other cross-linked polyolefins are resistant to the action of hydrocarbon solvents (Figure 61).

If the irradiation of polyethylene is performed under the proper conditions, and if the doses applied are relatively small — just as small as is required to improve the resistance of the polymer to heat — the electrical properties of the polymer remain practically unchanged /31, 70/. One such condition is that the irradiation be performed in an oxygen-free medium, in order to prevent the oxidation of the cross-linked polymer. It is also necessary to prevent any interaction of the "captured" free radicals with atmospheric oxygen following the irradiation. To do this, the cross-linked polymer is heated in an inert gas medium or in vacuo at a temperature close to the melting point or somewhat above it. This treatment results in a stabilization of the electrical parameters, probably owing to the sharp decrease in free radical concentration.

Photochemical cross-linking. Photochemical cross-linking of polyethylene by UV light in the presence of photosensitizers has evoked much interest in the course of the past few years. The mechanism of the process may be generally represented as follows. The sensitizer absorbs the energy of the UV light with formation of free radicals which accept hydrogen atoms from polyethylene chains. The macroradicals thus formed undergo recombination by forming cross-links between the chains /71/.

Chernyavskii /72/ made a survey of sensitizers which are suitable for photochemical cross-linking of polyethylene. Compounds used as sensitizers include benzophenone /71, 73 — 86/ and its derivatives /73, 76/, acetone /73/, acetophenone and its derivatives /73, 76/, benzil /76/, derivatives of anthraquinone /87/, aromatic hydrocarbons (benzene, naphthalene, anthracene, xylene, stilbene) /73, 76/, chlorinated aromatic and aliphatic hydrocarbons /71, 73, 81, 83, 84/, dyes (methylene blue, Bengal Red, etc.) /73/, diphenylamine /73, 74, 78/, sulfur monochloride /88 — 90/, PCl_3 /91, 93/ and other compounds.

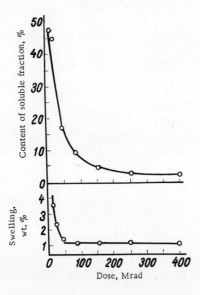

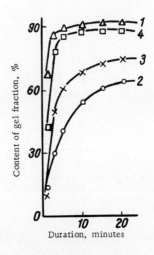

FIGURE 61. Solubility (in boiling o-xylene) and swelling (in o-xylene at 120°C during two hours) of the copolymer of ethylene with 3% α-butylene, as a function of the absorbed dose. Irradiation with 2.0 MeV electrons in helium /38/.

FIGURE 62. Kinetic curves of cross-linking of high-pressure polyethylene film, saturated with different sensitizers, exposed to UV light from two PRK-2 lamps at 2.5 cm distance from the film /84/:

1 — tetrachloroethylene; 2 — chloroform; 3 — carbon tetrachloride; 4 — benzophenone.

The process of photochemical cross-linking consists of two main stages: the introduction of the sensitizer and irradiation with UV light. The sensitizer is often introduced by saturating the polymer from the gas phase (chloroform, carbon tetrachloride, tetrachloroethylene, phosphorus trichloride) at room temperature or by heating the sensitizer (benzophenone) /84, 92, 94/. Figure 62 shows the yield of the gel fraction as a function of the effect of UV light on films of high-pressure polyethylene, saturated with different sensitizers. During the first few minutes of the irradiation the content of the gel fraction rapidly increases and attains its limiting value after only 10 minutes. If the irradiation intensity is low, the degree of cross-linking is directly proportional to the square root of the irradiation intensity /84/. Figure 63 shows the extent of cross-linking of polyethylene films saturated with tetrachloroethylene and benzophenone as a function of the intensity of the UV light and of the sensitizer content.

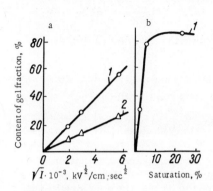

FIGURE 63. Content of gel fraction as a function of the light intensity (a) and sensitizer content (b) in high-pressure polyethylene film /84/:

1 — tetrachloroethylene; 2 — benzophenone.

Kachan et al. /84/ determined the probability ratio between degradation and cross-linking processes in polyethylene from the experimental data on the content of the sol fraction as a function of the reciprocal value of the duration of the irradiation, using the following formula /95/:

$$s + \sqrt{s} = \frac{P_0}{q_0} + \frac{1}{q_0 u_1 I t}$$

where s is the content of the sol fraction, P_0 is the number of cleavages in the main chain per number-average molecule, q_0 is the number of cross-links per number-average molecule, u_1 is the number-average degree of polymerization, I is the irradiation intensity and t is the duration of the irradiation.

The experimental values of P_0/q_0 are 0.40, 0.42, 0.71 and 0.86 respectively for benzophenone, tetrachloroethylene, carbon tetrachloride and chloroform used as sensitizers (irradiation with PRK-2 lamp). If most of the light is absorbed by the sensitizer and if the irradiation is of brief duration, the polymer chains cannot be degraded to a major extent, and it must be concluded that the values of P_0/q_0 reported in /84/ are somewhat high. This question must be further studied. It may be assumed, nevertheless, that one reason for the incompleteness of photosensitized cross-linking of polyethylene and hence also of high P_0/q_0 values is that the cross-linking process takes place mainly in amorphous regions.

Because of the difficulties involved in the cross-linking in the crystalline phase owing to the limited mobility of the chain, some of the polymer may fail to be cross-linked. If, in such cases, P_0/q_0 values are found from the equation $s + \sqrt{s} = f\,(1/t)$, they will not reflect the true ratio between the degradation and cross-linking rates and a correction will have to be introduced.

Photochemical cross-linking of polyethylene in the presence of PCl_3 as photosensitizer has been studied in fair detail /92, 96/. A gel fraction content of up to $85 - 90\%$ was obtained when up to $130\,\mu$ thick films of low-pressure, medium-pressure and high-pressure polyethylene and of a copolymer of ethylene with 7% propylene were saturated with PCl_3 vapors at room temperature during 2 minutes and then irradiated with UV light ($\lambda = 2,537$ Å) in the air for up to 4 minutes. Not more than $5 - 10\%$ phosphorus trichloride need be present in the polymer for the maximum degree of cross-linking to be obtained.

Irradiated PCl_3 is decomposed by light quanta into free radicals:

$$PCl_3 \xrightarrow{h\nu} \dot{P}Cl_2 + \dot{C}l$$

which are capable of accepting hydrogen atoms from hydrocarbon chains:

$$\cdots-CH_2-CH_2-CH_2-\cdots \xrightarrow{\dot{P}Cl_2,\ \dot{C}l} \cdots-CH_2-\dot{C}H_2-CH_2-\cdots$$

The cross-links between the chains are formed by recombination of the free radicals. The recombination acts seem to be preceded by a series of processes of free radical migration; the probability that the macroradicals react directly in the solid polymer is negligible /97/ and does not afford an explanation for the high yields of the gel fraction which are obtained within only a few minutes.

Elementary analysis showed that the cross-linked films contain up to 1% phosphorus. According to /98/, one way in which phosphorus is bound to the polymer is by the reaction between $\dot{P}Cl_2$ radicals with the macro-molecular chains at the site of the double bond in the chain:

$$\cdots-C=C-\cdots + \dot{P}Cl_2 \longrightarrow \cdots-\underset{\underset{PCl_2}{|}}{\overset{|}{C}}-\overset{|}{\underset{\cdot}{C}}-\cdots$$

$$\cdots-\underset{\underset{PCl_2}{|}}{\overset{|}{C}}-\overset{|}{\underset{\cdot}{C}}-\cdots + PCl_3 \longrightarrow \cdots-\underset{\underset{PCl_2}{|}}{\overset{|}{C}}-\underset{\underset{Cl}{|}}{\overset{|}{C}}-\cdots + \dot{P}Cl_2$$

$$\cdots-\underset{\underset{PCl_2}{|}}{\overset{|}{C}}-\underset{\underset{Cl}{|}}{\overset{|}{C}}-\cdots \xrightarrow{O_2,\ H_2O} \cdots-\overset{|}{C}-\overset{|}{C}-\cdots$$

This scheme is confirmed by spectroscopic data. Spectra of irradiated films have absorption bands at 980 and 1,180 cm^{-1}, corresponding to the bending vibrations of $-\overset{|}{\underset{\|}{P}}-OH$ and $-\overset{|}{\underset{|}{P}}=O$ groups /92/. In addition, a diminished concentration of double bonds was obtained as a result of cross-linking, as reflected by the decreased intensity of the 909 cm^{-1} band (Figure 64). Since the cross-linked products contain ionogenic groups, they take up basic dyes.

Seeing that the X-ray scattering curves of the initial and the cross-linked films are fully identical, we may assume that the cross-linking takes place mainly in the amorphous regions, while the crystalline regions remain essentially unaffected. Differences in secondary structures are noted when the modified and the unmodified films are deformed. It is seen in Figure 65 that when the cross-linked films are extended, fibrous structure is absent, while it is readily apparent in the initial film.

The most important property of photochemically cross-linked polymers is their high stability to heat. Films made of high-pressure polyethylene which, as is well known, loses all its tensile strength at a temperature as low as 110°C, retain a residual tensile strength of up to 10 kg/cm^2 at 200°C after they have been irradiated with UV in the presence of phosphorus trichloride. When heated at 4 degrees per minute under a load of 2 kg/cm^2, the modified film retained its original thickness up to 180°C. The yield point of the initial film under these conditions was 100°C (Figure 66).

Kachan et al. /99/ compared the processes of radiation-chemical and photochemical modification of polyethylene. Differences between the effects of UV light and ionizing radiation on polyethylene appear even in the stage of formation of macroradicals. The respective energies of C—H and C—C bonds in polyethylene molecules are known to be 4.28 and 3.44 eV. The most intense UV lines emitted by mercury quartz lamps at 2,537, 3,130 and 3,650 Å correspond to quantum energies of 4.88, 3.95 and 3.39 eV, which means that UV light of 2,537 and 3,130 Å can produce rupture of both types of bonds. The EPR spectrum /100/ of polyethylene irradiated with UV light at 77°K shows that $-CH_2-\dot{C}H_2$ radicals are formed in preference to $-CH_2-\dot{C}H-CH_2-$ radicals, which means that the acts of degradation of the main chains predominate over the acts of cross-linking. The quantum energies of ionizing radiations, on the contrary, are much higher than chemical bond energies, which means that macroradicals can be formed in any part of the macromolecular chain at a much faster rate than during irradiation with UV light. The formation of one macroradical in polyethylene at 77°K requires 110 eV of UV energy /100/, as against only 30 eV of energy of ionizing radiation /101/. It follows that macroradicals are much more effectively formed by the action of ionizing radiation than by the photochemical process; this is in agreement with experiment, which shows that intense UV irradiation for not less than 100 hours is needed to form a tridimensional structure in polyethylene, while under a beam of ionizing radiation such cross-linking may be attained much more rapidly (Figure 67).

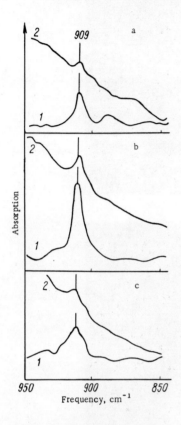

FIGURE 64. IR spectra of low-pressure (a), medium-pressure (b) and high-pressure (c) polyethylene /96/:

1 — initial films; 2 — films which have been photochemically cross-linked in the presence of phosphorus trichloride.

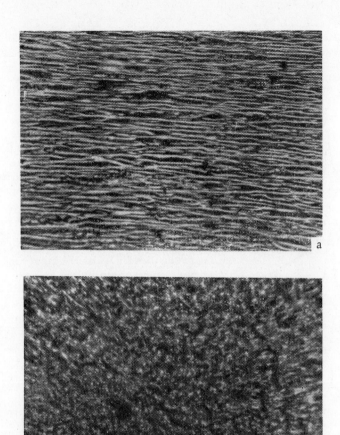

FIGURE 65. Microphotograph of films of the copolymer of ethylene with 7% propylene, 300% stretched /96/:

a — initial film; b — film after photochemical cross-linking in the presence of phosphorus trichloride. Magnification 300×.

While radiation-chemical cross-linking is much more effective than the photochemical process, fairly large doses (up to 70 − 100 Mrad) of ionizing radiation are still required to attain a high content (90 − 95%) of the gel fraction. The effectiveness of radiation-chemical cross-linking of polyethylene and polypropylene may be enhanced by the addition of polyfunctional monomers (see, for instance, /102, 103/), which exert a sensitizing effect by forming cross-links between the chains:

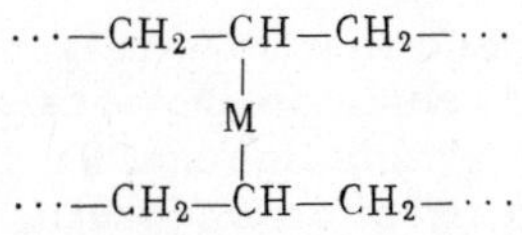

$$\cdots—CH_2—CH—CH_2—\cdots$$
$$\mid$$
$$M$$
$$\mid$$
$$\cdots—CH_2—CH—CH_2—\cdots$$

where M is a bifunctional monomer.

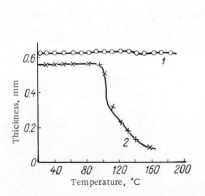

FIGURE 66. Flow curves of photochemically modified (1) and unmodified (2) films of high-pressure polyethylene /96/.

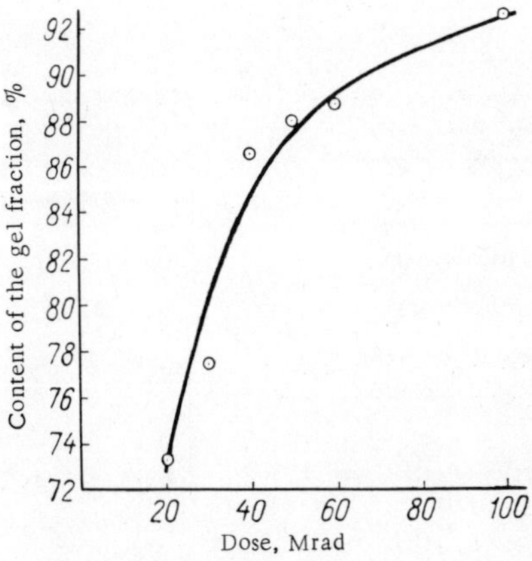

FIGURE 67. Content of gel fraction as a function of the absorbed dose. High-pressure polyethylene irradiated with fast electrons (energy 2 MeV, dose rate 1 Mrad/min) /99/.

Compounds which sensitize photochemical cross-linking, far from accelerating, may even inhibit radiation-chemical cross-linking. Kachan et al. /104/ noted such an inhibition and explained it by postulating a recombination of macroradicals with the radicals of the additives under the action of ionizing radiation.

Processes which accompany the effect of ionizing irradiation carried out in the air have already been discussed. It has been seen that, in order to prevent the interaction of "captured" radicals with atmospheric oxygen, cross-linking of polyolefins and thermal treatment of the cross-linked polymers must be effected out of contact with oxygen. Since UV irradiation produces a relatively small number of macroradicals, photochemical cross-linking, unlike radiation-chemical cross-linking, may be effected in the air, and subsequent thermal treatment of the polymer is unnecessary.

Radiation-chemical and photochemical cross-linking also produce different changes in the double bonds of the resulting polymer. Ionizing radiation increases the number of double bonds in polyethylene. The main type of unsaturated groupings thus formed are trans-vinylene groups, which give a band at 965 cm^{-1} in the infrared. Owing to the increased concentration of the double bonds with increasing radiation dose, the material becomes brown. The content of terminal double bonds, which give a band at 909 cm^{-1}, remains practically unchanged /31/. The intensity of the 909 cm^{-1} band decreases, on the contrary, as a result of cross-linking

101

which has been photosensitized with PCl_3 (Figure 64). The difference between the two methods of cross-linking consists in the different penetrating power of ionizing radiation and UV light. The radiation-chemical method is used to effect cross-linking in thick-walled articles, while photochemical cross-linking, which can be employed only in thin layers (up to $200-250\,\mu$), can be used to modify the properties of films or surface layers of finished articles.

TABLE 15. Comparative table of photochemical and radiation-chemical methods of cross-linking of polyolefins

	Photochemical method	Radiation-chemical method
Radiation sources	UV lamps	Electron accelerators, Co^{60}
Radiation energy	Up to 5 eV	Up to $1-3$ MeV
Depth of polyolefin material showing radiation effects	About 0.2 mm	For γ-radiation (1.3 MeV) about 300 mm; for 1.2 MeV β-particles about 6 mm
Identity of sensitizers (additives)	Ketones, aldehydes, PCl_3, etc.	Polyfunctional monomers, nitrous oxide, sulfur chloride, etc.
Use of sensitizers (additives)	Required	Reduces the radiation dose
Effect of sensitizers (additives)	Absorption of UV energy, decomposition to free radicals, acceptance of hydrogen atoms from macromolecules, formation of $C-C$ cross-links between main chains	Mostly act as cross-linking agents when the macromolecules are activated by radiation
Atmosphere required to prevent extensive degradation by radiation	Air or inert gas	Inert gas*
Unsaturation	Decreases in the case of PCl_3	Increases
Post effect	Absent	Oxidation of "captured" macroradicals

* At moderate radiation doses.

The two cross-linking methods also display similar features. The changes in the heat resistance and in the main physicomechanical parameters of the polymers produced by the two techniques are quite similar.

A comparison of the photochemical and radiation-chemical methods of cross-linking is shown in Table 15.

It is seen that the photochemical method is preferably employed to modify thin polyethylene articles or surfaces of thick-walled articles. The advantages of this method compared to the radiation-chemical method are the simplicity and cheapness of the apparatus required and the fact that the treatment can be carried out in the air.

Bibliography

1. Busse, W. F. and M. A. Smook. — India Rubber World, 128:348. 1953.
2. Busse, W. F. and F. W. Bilmeyer. — J. Polymer Sci., 12(67):599. 1954.
3. Smook, M. A., W. J. Remington, and D. E. Strain. — In: Polythene. The Technology and Uses of Ethylene Polymers (edited by A. Renfrew and P. Morgan), New York, Interscience. 2nd edition, 1960.
4. U. S. Patent 2416060. 1947.
5. Smook, M. A., J. D. Roche, and W. B. Clark. — India Rubber World, 128:54. 1953.
6. Italian Patent 563508. 1956.
7. Bier, G. — Angew. Chem., 73:186. 1961.
8. Manásek, Z. and D. Bellus. Polipropilen (Polypropylene), p. 126, edited by V. I. Pilipovskii and I. K. Yartsev. — Izdatel'stvo "Khimiya." 1967.
9. Natta, G., G. Crespi, and M. Bruzzone. — Chim. Ind., 42:463. 1960.
10. Jones, G.—In: Chemical Reactions of Polymers (edited by E. Fettis). New York, J. Wiley. 1964.
11. Leonard, E. C., W. E. Loed, J. H. Mason, and J. A. Stenstrom. — J. Polymer Sci., 55:799. 1961.
12. Leonard, E. C., W. E. Loed, J. H. Mason, and W. L. Wheelwright. — J. Appl. Polymer Sci., 5:157. 1961.
13. British Patent 849058. 1960.
14. U. S. Patent 2906743. 1960.
15. Italian Patent 537429. 1955.
16. Italian Patent 591501. 1958.
17. British Patent 811848. 1959.
18. British Patent 867209. 1961.
19. Seidov, N. M. Novyi sinteticheskii kauchuk na osnove etilena i propilena (New Synthetic Rubber Based on Ethylene and Propylene), p. 95. — Azerbaidzhanskoe Gosudarstvennoe Izdatel'stvo, Baku. 1966.
20. Amberg, L. O. — In: Vulcanization of Elastomers (edited by G. Alliger and I. Sjothun), New York, Reinhold. 1964.
21. U. S. Patent 2626248. 1953.
22. U. S. Patent 2681327. 1954.
23. Brown, H. P. and C. F. Gibbs. — Ind. Eng. Chem., 47:1006. 1955.
24. French Patent 1336464. 1964.
25. Bonotto, S. and C. L. Purcell.— Mod. Plastics, 42(7):135, 140, 198. 1965.
26. Rees, R. and D. Vaughan. — Polymer Preprints, Vol. 6, No. 1. 1965.
27. Semenova, A. S. and A. F. Nikolaev.— Plast. Massy, No. 10:67. 1967.
28. Chem. Engng., 71(22):90. 1964.
29. Brit. Plastics, 38(5):262. 1965.

30. Bovey, F.A. The Effects of Ionizing Radiation on Natural and Synthetic High Polymers. — New York, Interscience. 1958.

31. Charlesby, A. Atomic Radiation and Polymers. — London, Pergamon Press. 1960.

32. Swallow, A.J. Radiation Chemistry of Organic Compounds. — London, Pergamon Press. 1960.

33. Bolt, R.O. and J.G. Carrol. Radiation Effects on Organic Materials. — London, Academic Press. 1963.

34. Shultz, A. — In: Chemical Reactions of Polymers (edited by E. Fettes), New York, Wiley. 1964.

35. Basket, A.C. and C.W. Miller. — Nature, 174:364. 1954.

36. Schumacher, K. — Kolloid Z., 157:16. 1958.

37. Sirota, A.G., A.L. Gol'denberg, P.A. Il'chenko, E.P. Ryabikov, B.G. Fedotov, M.G. Karaseva, L.I. Zyuzina, and O.K. Kharitonova. — Plast. Massy, No. 8:58. 1966.

38. Sirota, A.G., B.G. Fedotov, E.P. Ryabikov, P.A. Il'chenko, V.M. Zapletnyak, V.I. Aleshin, and A.L. Gol'denberg. — Plast. Massy, No. 2:3. 1967.

39. Black, R.M. and B.J. Lyons. — Nature, 180:1346. 1957.

40. Black, R.M. and B.J. Lyons. — Proc. Roy. Soc., London, A253:322. 1959.

41. Veselovskii, R.A., S.S. Leshchenko, and V.L. Karpov. — In: "Radiatsionnaya khimiya polimerov," p. 268, Izdatel'stvo "Nauka." 1966.

42. Cooper, G.D. and A.R. Gilbert. — J. Polymer Sci., 38:275. 1959.

43. Loy, B.R. — J. Polymer Sci., A1:2251. 1963.

44. Lawton, E.J., A.M. Bueche, and J.S. Balwit. — Nature, 172:76. 1953.

45. Alexander, P., R.M. Black, and A. Charlesby. — Proc. Roy. Soc., London, A232:31, 1955.

46. Charlesby, A. and W.H.T. Davison. — Chem. Ind., London, 8:232. 1957.

47. Charlesby, A. and A.J. Swallow. — Rev. Phys. Chem., 10:289. 1959.

48. Charlesby, A., E. Arnim, and L. Callaghan. — Intern. J. Appl. Radiation Isotopes, 3:226. 1958.

49. Kitamura, R. and L. Mandelkern. — J. Am. Chem. Soc., 86(17):3529. 1964.

50. Epstein, L.M. — J. Polymer Sci. 26:399. 1957.

51. Lawton, E.J., J.S. Balwit, and R.S. Powell. — J. Polymer Sci., 32:257. 1958.

52. Lawton, E.J., R.S. Powell, and J.S. Balwit. — J. Polymer Sci., 32:277. 1958.

53. Williams, T.F. and M. Dole. — J. Am. Chem. Soc., 81:2919. 1959.

54. Levy, B. — J. Appl. Polymer Sci., 5:408. 1961; Trans. Am. Nucl. Soc., 4:124. 1961.

55. Sirota, A.G., B.G. Fedotov, E.P. Ryabikov, A.L. Gol'denberg, P.A. Il'chenko, and O.K. Kharitonova. — Doklady AN SSSR, Seriya khim., 183(2):393. 1968.

56. Black, R. M. and A. Charlesby. — Intern. J. Appl. Radiation Isotopes, 7:126. 1959.
57. Black, R. M. — Nature, 178(4528):305. 1956.
58. British Patent 740899. 1955.
59. U. S. Patent 2877500. 1959.
60. U. S. Patent 2878174. 1959.
61. U. S. Patent 2904480. 1959.
62. Ushakov, G. P., Yu. A. Gushcho, Yu. S. Lazurkin, and V. S. Kazakov. — Vysokomolekulyarnye Soedineniya, 2(10):1512. 1960.
63. Maigel'dinov, I. A. — In: "Khimiya i fiziko-khimiya vysokomolekulyarnykh soedinenii," p. 196, Izdatel'stvo AN SSSR. 1952.
64. Samoilov, A. V. — Plast. Massy, No. 5:14. 1967.
65. Nalivaiko, E. I. and A. G. Sirota. — Plast. Massy, No. 9:14. 1967.
66. Houdret, C. and A. Lamm. — Rev. Gen. Caoutchouc, 40(9):1323. 1963.
67. Liebling, G. — J. Appl. Polymer Sci., 6(22):461. 1962.
68. Vlagin, G. — Mater. Plast., 3(4):209. 1966.
69. Nalivaiko, E. I. and A. G. Sirota. — Plast. Massy, No. 2:13. 1968.
70. Vlasenko, V. P., V. L. Karpov, E. P. Rashina, and E. E. Finkel'. — In: "Radiatsionnaya khimiya polimerov," p. 325, Izdatel'stvo "Nauka." 1966.
71. Charlesby, A., C. S. Grace, and F. B. Pilkington. — Proc. Roy. Soc., 268A(1333):205. 1962.
72. Chernyavskii, G. V. — Author's Summary of Candidate's Thesis, Kiev. 1967.
73. Wilski, H. — Angew. Chem., 71:612. 1959.
74. Oster, G. — J. Polymer Sci., 22:185. 1956.
75. British Patent 848414. 1960.
76. Oster, G., G. K. Oster, and H. Moroson. — J. Polymer Sci., 34:671. 1959.
77. Charlesby, A., C. S. Grace, and L. C. Penhale. — J. Polymer Sci., 34:681. 1959.
78. Chien Pao-kun, Ping-chêng Chien, and Eng-chiang Hao. — Vysokomolekulyarnye Soedineniya, 1:635. 1959.
79. Liang Yang-chin, Hsia-yu Fang, Ping-chêng Chiang, and Pao-kung Chien. — Scientia Sinica, 11:903. 1962.
80. Chien Pao-kung, Wên-chêng Chiang, Yü-chêng Liao, and Ying-chin Liang. — Scientia Sinica, 11:1513. 1962.
81. Wilski, H. — Kolloid Z., 188:4. 1963.
82. French Patent 1369014. 1964.
83. Kachan, A. A., G. V. Chernyavskii, and V. A. Shrubovich. — Dopovidi AN URSR, 10:1312. 1966.
84. Kachan, A. A., G. V. Chernyavskii, and V. A. Shrubovich. — Vysokomolekulyarnye Soedineniya, 95(1):43. 1967.
85. British Patent 981255. 1965.
86. Uematsu Ititaro. — J. Soc. Rubber Ind. Japan, 32(11):902. 1959.

87. Oster, G. — J. Polymer Sci., B32:1181. 1964.

88. Wilski, H. — Kunststoffe, 52:471. 1962.

89. Kaurkova, G.K., A.A. Kachan, K.A. Kornev and L.L. Chervyatsova. — Khimichna Promislovist', No. 2:8. 1965.

90. GFR Patent 1167018. 1964.

91. Soviet Patent 191114. 1965; Byulleten' Izobretatelya, No. 3. 1967.

92. Kachan, A.A., G.V. Chernyavskii, and V.A. Shrubovich. — Vysokomolekulyarnye Soedineniya, A9(5):107. 1967.

93. Kachan, A.A. et al. — Tezisy dokladov na Vsesoyuznom nauchno-tekhnicheskom soveshchanii po plastmassam, p. 48. 1966.

94. Kachan, A.A., G.V. Chernyavskii, and V.A. Shrubovich. — Vysokomolekulyarnye Soedineniya, B9(1):40. 1967.

95. Charlesby, A., S.H. Pinner. — Proc. Roy. Soc., 249A:367. 1959.

96. Kachan, A.A., V.A. Shrubovich, G.V. Chernyavskii, A.G. Sirota, E.P. Ryabikov, A.L. Gol'denberg, P.A. Il'chenko, G.A. Patrikeev, V.N. Manin, V.S. Erofeev, G.L. Inikhov, A.N. Gromov, and M.A. Kovalkin. — Plast. Massy, No. 6:7. 1968.

97. Bresler, S.E., E.N. Kazbekov, V.N. Fomichev, F. Sech, and P. Smeitek. — Fizika Tverdogo Tela, 5(2):675. 1963.

98. Kharasch, M., E. Jensen, and U.P. Urry. — J. Am. Chem. Soc., 67:1864. 1945.

99. Kachan, A.A., A.G. Sirota, G.V. Chernyavskii, and V.A. Shrubovich. — Vysokomolekulyarnye Soedineniya, 10A(3):471. 1968.

100. Ranby, B. and H. Joshida. — J. Polymer Sci., C10:263. 1966.

101. Lawton, E.J., J.S. Balwit, and R.S. Powell. — J. Chem. Phys., 33(395):405. 1960.

102. Egorova, Z.S., V.L. Karpov, S.S. Leshchenko, L.V. Mitrofanova, N.A. Slovokhotova, A.P. Tumanova, and E.E. Finkel'. — In: "Radiatsionnaya khimiya polimerov," p. 285, Izdatel'stvo "Nauka." 1966.

103. Batychko, S.V., R.P Braginzkii, E.G. Yarmilko, and A.M. Kabakchi. — In: "Radiatsionnaya khimiya polimerov," p. 282, Izdatel'stvo "Nauka." 1966.

104. Kachan, A.A., G.V. Chernyavskii, and V.A. Shrubovich. — Dopovidi AN URSR, No. 7: 626. 1967.

Chapter VI

FORMULATIONS BASED ON POLYOLEFINS

COMPOUNDING POLYOLEFINS WITH
DIFFERENT POLYMERS

Compounding polyolefins with each other or with other types of polymers makes it possible to produce major changes in the resulting material in the desired direction. Thus, polypropylene compounded with high-density or low-density polyethylene /1−3/ has a lower brittleness temperature than polypropylene. Plochocki /4/, who studied the properties of mixtures of isotactic polypropylene and linear polyethylene, showed that the technological properties of mixtures are superior to those of the starting polymers. The flow melt index of the mixtures is higher than those of the individual components within a very wide range of polypropylene-to-polyethylene ratios (15:85, 25:75, 50:50, 75:25).

If polyethylene and ethylene-propylene copolymers are introduced simultaneously into polypropylene, the impact strength and the physico-mechanical parameters at low temperatures will be improved /5, 6/.

A significant decrease in the brittleness temperature and an increase in the impact strength result from the mixing of polypropylene with polyisobutylene and different rubbers /7−9/. This is, however, accompanied by a decrease in the tensile strength of the material (Figure 68). The yield point of the polypropylene-polyisobutylene mixture decreases with increasing content of the latter polymer in the mixture /10/. These mixtures are rubberlike in a wide temperature range — between the vitrification point of polyisobutylene and the melting point of polypropylene. The higher the content of polyisobutylene, the more pronounced are the rubberlike properties.

Some of the parameters of the mixtures do not vary monotonically with the composition; these include the elongation at break. If the polypropylene : polyisobutylene ratio is close to 1:1, this elongation is at a minimum (Figure 69, curve 1). The existence of this minimum is due to two different deformation mechanisms. Polyisobutylene, which is the amorphous component of the mixture, is capable of sustaining large reversible elastic deformations. If the stiffer, crystalline polypropylene is now added, the elasticity modulus increases and the deformability decreases. The highly crystalline component of the mixture — isotactic polypropylene — gives large forced rubberlike deformations if a sufficiently large stress is applied. The addition of polyisobutylene reduces the tensile strength of polypropylene and prevents the stresses from becoming large enough to effect such forced rubberlike deformations. As a result, the elongation at break decreases.

If the composition of the mixture is altered, this deformation mechanism is replaced by the other. The minimum elongation at break corresponds to the intermediate composition range, in which neither mechanism can become fully operative.

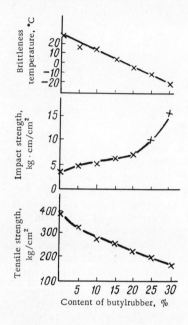

FIGURE 68. Properties of compositions of polypropylene with butylrubber as a function of the content of the latter component /7/.

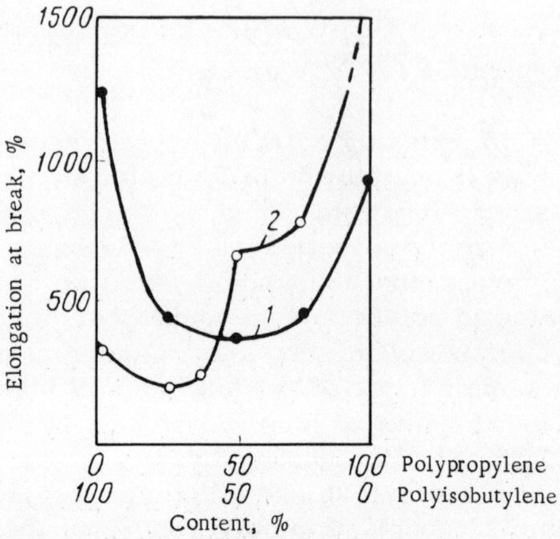

FIGURE 69. Elongation at break as a function of the composition of a mixture of polypropylene and polyisobutylene at 23°C (1) and 60°C (2) /10/.

At elevated temperatures the curve giving the elongation at break as a function of the component ratio in the mixture consists of two parts (Figure 69, curve 2), corresponding, respectively, to low and high contents of the amorphous component in the mixture. This is explained by the decrease in the deformability of polyisobutylene at elevated temperatures owing to fluidity, which interferes with the development of large rubberlike deformations. As the polypropylene ratio in the mixture increases, the fluidity becomes smaller and the tendency to rubberlike deformations is enhanced. These effects, which are also noted in the study of specially prepared mixtures of amorphous with crystalline polypropylene, are considered /10/ to be a consequence of the fact that a system consisting of amorphous and crystalline polymer is a two-phase system. From this point of view a change in the composition of the mixture amounts to a transition from an amorphous system filled with the crystalline component to a crystalline system filled with the amorphous component. This transition is accompanied by a sudden change in the relationship between the physico-mechanical parameters and the composition of the mixture.

Compositions of polyethylene with polyisobutylene and nonpolar rubbers, which are extensively employed, have been studied in much detail /11 — 20/. The compounding usually takes place in closed mixers at 130 — 170°C or on rollers. The main result of the introduction of polyisobutylene is the enhancement of elasticity in polyethylene and of resistance to cracking under prolonged external stresses and under the action of surfactants. As the polyisobutylene content increases, the tensile strength, elasticity modulus, hardness and elongation at break all decrease. According to /11, 13, 14, 16/, the variation in the physicomechanical parameters, including the elongation at break, with the composition is continuous. It was shown, however, by Slonimskii et al. /18/ who, unlike other workers, did not study roller-compounded materials but those precipitated from solution in decalin, that the variation of the elongation with the composition passes through a minimum. At room temperature this minimum corresponds to a poly-ethylene : polyisobutylene ratio of about 3 : 1. The reason is clearly the same as that explained above for the compositions of polypropylene with polyisobutylene. That this minimum was not found in specimens prepared by roller milling or by compounding in mixing vessels is probably due to additional homogenization by chemical reactions taking place between the components which result in the formation of block and graft copolymers.

The properties of mixtures of crystalline polyolefins, say, mixtures of polyethylene with isotactic polypropylene, are determined by their inhomo-geneous structure /21/. Microscopic studies of the mixture in polarized light revealed large spherulites of polypropylene and small spherulites of polyethylene. The yield point of the mixture increased with increasing content of polypropylene. The tensile strength of polyethylene-polypropylene mixtures increased with increasing proportion of polypropylene in the mixture. As distinct from the individual components, which can undergo large forced rubberlike deformations at room temperature, the mixtures fail at 20°C as a result of very small deformations (10% extension). However, the deformability of the mixture substantially increases above the melting point of polyethylene, which is the lower-melting component. Thus, polyethylene acts here as a high-molecular plasticizer of polypropylene /21, 22/.

Obviously, a similar deformational behavior may also be expected in mixtures of other pairs of crystalline polyolefins which are inhomogeneous owing to the separate crystallization of the components. Thus, the inhomo-geneity of the mixture accounts for the low values of elongation at break and of the tensile strength of compositions containing high-pressure and low-pressure polyethylene /23/ (Figure 70). The plasticizing effect of high-pressure polyethylene in mixture with low-pressure polyethylene probably accounts for the increased resistance to embrittlement displayed by low-pressure polyethylene on the addition of 15 to 50 parts by weight of high-pressure polyethylene /24/.

The introduction of various amorphous polymers into crystalline poly-olefins results in changes in important technical properties of the material. Thus, if polypropylene is mixed with amorphous polymers, its dye takeup /25 — 29/, resistance to frost /30/, resistance to light /31/, and resistance to heat /32/ all increase, and its creep decreases /33/. The increase in the dye takeup is particularly marked if polar polymer additives are introduced, but the mixtures will then not be homogeneous. The utilization of nonpolar and low-polar polymers results in the formation of less inhomogeneous mixtures with polyolefins, which take up disperse dyes owing to the looseness of the compounded structure.

When small amounts of polystyrene or a copolymer of styrene with 20% acrylonitrile were added to a fiber made of isotactic polypropylene, a loosening in the fiber structure was noted /29/. In the presence of as little as 5% of these additives, the stress which must be applied to effect an extension of the fiber decreased. It is assumed that the microparticles of the second component, which are distributed in the polypropylene, loosen its structure and reduce the resistance to the shift of structural elements with respect to one another during the deformation. The looseness of the structure is also indicated by the much greater absorption of dyes by the fiber which contains the additive.

Compositions of polyolefins with natural polymers are known, in particular with cellulose /34/, and a mixture of polypropylene with lignin /35 − 40/. Lignin is of potential interest as the active component of the mixture. If a mixture of polypropylene with alkaline sulfate lignin is heated at about 200°C, the constituents interact with formation of a partly cross-linked structure. The maximum formation of the gel fraction is attained if the content of lignin in the polypropylene is about 2%. The introduction of a small amount of lignin does not alter the crystalline structure of the material, but it enhances its resistance to heat and its stability to photochemical aging.

An important problem which is connected with the determination of the compositions and conditions of compounding is the compatibility of the components of the polyolefin-based mixtures. The literature data on the subject are contradictory. Thus, students of the structure and properties of mixtures of polyethylene with polypropylene came to different conclusions

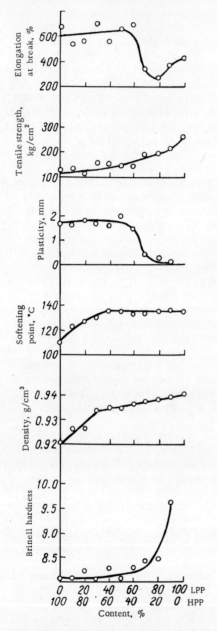

FIGURE 70. Various parameters as a function of the composition of a mixture of high-pressure polyethylene (HPP) with low-pressure polyethylene (LPP) /23/.

regarding their compatibility. Mikhailov et al. /22/ studied mixtures of low-pressure polyethylene with isotactic polypropylene. They obtained differential thermal analysis curves, which show one endothermal effect corresponding to a polyethylene content in the mixture of 75% or higher. At smaller polyethylene concentrations two endothermal effects are noted, which correspond to the melting temperature ranges of individual components of the mixture. Mixtures with high contents of polyethylene have high heat capacities and their densities differ from the additive values, and it was accordingly concluded that, within a certain range of component ratios, polyethylene and polypropylene are compatible. The highest compatibility is displayed by mixtures containing 75% polyethylene. The compatibility is explained by these authors in terms of the plasticizing effect of polyethylene on polypropylene; the high flexibility of polyethylene chains reduces the stiffness of polypropylene, which accounts for the compatibility, and for the fact that it occurs in mixtures having a relatively high polyethylene content.

Slonimskii et al. /21/ also studied the compatibility of isotactic polypropylene with polyethylene. He made certain optical tests of the structure and concluded that the mixtures were inhomogeneous and the components incompatible. This conclusion is in agreement with the results of other workers /41, 42/, who studied the spherulite structures of mixtures of polypropylene and polyethylene.

Gul' et al. /43/, on the contrary, consider that polyethylene and polypropylene are thermodynamically compatible. Their conclusions are based on the determination of the optical densities of films made from a mixture of polyethylene and polypropylene in the ratio 1 : 2, which had been thermally treated. They noted that the optical density decreased with increasing duration of heating; in their view this is due to a decrease in the microheterogeneity as a result of diffusional processes. The fact that the tensile strength curves of mixtures become less disperse as the mixtures are heated also speaks in favor of increased homogeneity.

Fil'bert et al. /44/ made a detailed study of mixtures of isotactic polypropylene with low-pressure polyethylene. The content of polypropylene was varied between 5 and 25%. The differential thermal analysis curves had two peaks, corresponding to endothermal effects at the melting points of the individual polymers. The crystallinity of polypropylene found from the spectroscopic data (absorption bands at 845 and 1,170 cm^{-1}) did not change on the addition of polyethylene. The absorption coefficient at frequencies corresponding to the bending vibrations of methylene groups in polyethylene (731 cm^{-1}) proved to be independent of the component ratio in the mixture. This was interpreted as indicating that polypropylene is incompatible with polyethylene and that they crystallize in the mixture as individual compounds. The nonadditive values of densities and heat capacities of the mixtures, which had been previously /22/ regarded as indicating the compatibility of polypropylene with polyethylene, were interpreted by Fil'bert et al. /44/ as being due to the formation of mixed spherulites containing the smaller crystalline formations of both polyethylene and polypropylene; this is equivalent to saying that the two components are incompatible on the molecular, but compatible on the supermolecular level.

Data on the compatibility of polyethylene with polyisobutylene are also contradictory. According to some workers /15, 17/, they are compatible; according to others, they are not /12, 16/. The incompatibility of the two compounds has been demonstrated by X-ray studies /12/. The mixture displays a decreasing crystallinity with increasing content of the poly-isobutylene component, while the average size of the crystalline regions remains unchanged; it follows that polyisobutylene is distributed in amorphous regions of polyethylene, with formation of a discrete amorphous phase, with a short-range order of the molecules (6.1 Å), which differs from that of the amorphous phase of polyethylene (4.55 Å). According to /16/, full compatibility of polyethylene with polyisobutylene is not attained even above the melting point of polyethylene, when both the polymers are amorphous.

The different conclusions arrived at by different workers as to compatibilities of two different polymers are largely due to the lack of an agreed definition of this term.

It seems expedient to distinguish between thermodynamic and service compatibilities /43, 45, 46/. Thermodynamically compatible polymers do not alter their properties when their temperature is raised and then brought back to the initial value. The degree of homogeneity of the mixture can also increase as a result. It has been suggested that the degree of thermo-dynamic compatibility be estimated by means of the range of component ratios within which the system is thermodynamically stable; the wider the range of component ratios within which the polymers are mutually miscible, the higher their compatibility. In view of the complexity of chain structure and chain associations, it is difficult to assume that polyolefins are compatible with each other or with other polymers. The stability of the structures and the properties of mixtures of polyolefins may be due not to their thermodynamic condition, but to the slowness of changes occurring in their structures. However, thermodynamic incompatibility need not interfere with service compatibility, which depends on the size of tolerable changes in the properties of the material with time during its service life. Such changes in a mixture of thermodynamically incompatible polymers are connected with the increasing inhomogeneity of the system.

Accordingly, polyethylene and polypropylene are thermodynamically incompatible, while being compatible in service. Polar polymers, too, may be service-compatible with polyolefins. An example is a mixture of polyethylene with poly(vinyl alcohol) in the ratio of 95 : 5, which is resistant to oils /46/.

FILLED POLYOLEFINS

Filling is employed to increase stiffness (Figure 71), to raise the yield point and to improve other important properties in the exploitation of polyolefins as construction materials. Various powderlike and fibrous materials may serve as fillers: alumina, silica, magnesia, aluminum silicate, powdered metals (Fe, Cu, Ni, Al, etc.), fiber glass, asbestos, lamp black, wood meal, etc. /47 — 54; 17, p. 128/. The properties of the composition will depend not only on the identity and the content of the filler, but also on the shape of the particles and on the form of their surface. Thus, polyethylene filled with dendritic iron powder becomes much stronger than polyethylene filled with iron powder, the particles of which are platelet-shaped /51/.

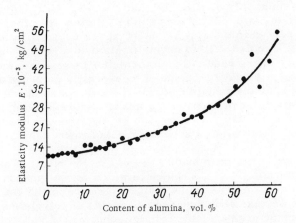

FIGURE 71. Flexural modulus of high-density polyethylene as a function of the content of alumina filler /48/.

Akutin et al. /55/ studied the IR spectra of a formulation of polyethylene with titanium dioxide and found absorption bands at 1,515 and 1,430 cm^{-1}, which were not present in the spectra of the individual components; the intensity of the absorption in the $1,000-1,200$ cm^{-1} range also increased. These details of the spectrum, which were ascribed to the appearance of the bonds $Ti-O-R$, led the authors to the conclusion that TiO_2 reacts with polyethylene during compounding and subsequent treatment of the composition at elevated temperatures with formation of surface compounds of the type

$$
\begin{array}{c}
(O-Ti-O-)_mH \\
| \\
\cdots-CH_2-CH_2-C-CH_2-CH_2-\cdots \\
| \\
H
\end{array}
$$

Since the structure of polyolefins is heterogeneous, it is necessary to consider not only the interaction of the filler surface with the macro-molecular chain, but mainly with the supermolecular structures. The nature, dispersity and other characteristics of the filler determine the morphology and size of supermolecular formations and thus also the properties of the composition. Thus, different results are obtained when aminated /56/ and unmodified /57/ Aerosil are introduced into polyethylene. Filling with unmodified Aerosil has no effect on the morphology and size of spherulites; the particles of this filler, which has a polymer-repellant surface, tend to form aggregates. Aminated Aerosil, on the contrary, is distributed in polyethylene in a more uniform manner. If present even in small (0.1%) amounts, the structure is loosened and the filler extends the separation between the spherulites.

Additives which alter the structure of supermolecular formations and which are introduced in small amounts are not fillers in the proper sense of the word. Such structure-forming additives may be fine mineral dispersions such as silica, silicates, NaCl, $CaCl_2$, $AlCl_3$, sodium and aluminum sulfates, etc. /58/. Fine solid particles, less than 1 μ in diameter, dispersed in the polymer melt, act as crystallization nuclei when the melt is cooled. Rapid crystallization on a large number of heterogeneous centers results in the formation of smaller, more uniform spherulite structures. Films made of high-density polyethylene compounded with polypropylene and containing 0.25 − 3 wt.% of a solid mineral substance with particle diameter of about 50 mμ are transparent owing to the fine spherulite structure; they are also less brittle, probably owing to the relatively small dimensions and considerable homogeneity of the spherulites /58/.

A detailed study has been made /59 − 66/ on the effect of artifact crystallization nuclei,— i.e., substances which do not interact with the polymer and which melt above the melting temperature of the polymer — on the supermolecular structure and properties of polyolefins. Such substances include organic acids (adipic, sebacic) and salts of heavy metals with organic acids such as bismuth salicylate, titanium oxalate, titanium acetate, lead benzoate, lead palmitate, zinc acetate and cobalt naphthionate. When such crystallization nuclei were introduced (the most effective dose was 0.15 − 0.2 wt.%), the mechanical strength, deformability and recrystallization potential of polyethylene and polypropylene increased.

Low-pressure polyethylene and polypropylene containing organic acid salts in concentrations between 0.4 and 1.5 wt.% are more stable to deformational, thermal and photochemical forces.

An important consequence of the alteration of the supermolecular structure of polyethylene by the presence of artifact crystallization nuclei is an increased resistance of the material to cracking /67, 68/. Figure 72 shows the increased cracking resistance of low-pressure polyethylene under the simultaneous effect of a bending load and 20% aqueous solution of a surfactant (OP-7 emulsifier) at 50°C. A considerable increase in the resistance to cracking can also be attained by introducing very small amounts of organic compounds which melt above the melting point of the polymer: anthranilic, adipic and sebacic acids and mannitol /67 − 69/ (Table 16). The strong effect produced by the addition of very small amounts of such structurizing substances

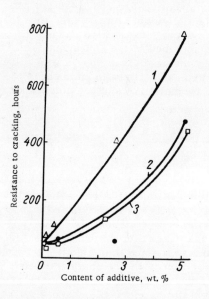

FIGURE 72. Resistance of low-pressure polyethylene to cracking as a function of the content of mineral additives /67/:

1 − $Al_2O_3 \cdot SiO_2$; 2 − SiO_2; 3 − TiO_2.

is probably due to the satisfactory distribution of the additive in the polymer melt. It is possible, moreover, that these compounds affect the crystallization kinetics not only in their capacity as crystallization centers, but also as surface-active substances which reduce the tension at the melt-solid interface.

TABLE 16. Effect of added surfactants on the cracking resistance of low-pressure polyethylene /67/

Additive	M.p. of additive, °C	Content of additive, wt. %	Resistance to cracking, hours	Tensile strength, kg/cm²	Elongation at break, %
None	—	—	50	204	509
Anthranilic acid . . .	144—145	0.1	1,000	215	505
		0.01	670	204	475
		0.001	60	213	345
Adipic acid	153	0.1	670	207	370
		0.01	760	215	419
		0.001	1,000	207	306
Sebacic acid	134.5	0.1	770	201	366
		0.01	320	217	586
		0.001	50	204	516
Mannitol	166	0.1	580	213	500
		0.01	400	207	509
		0.001	205	201	480

The effect of surface-active structurization agents makes it possible to attain a considerable increase in the resistance of polyethylene to cracking without at the same time impairing its dielectric properties in a significant manner. Table 17 shows comparative data on the dielectric properties of crack-resistant formulations which include surface-active structure-forming agents and mineral dispersions (aluminum silicate).

TABLE 17. Effect of added surfactants and aluminosilicate on the properties of low-pressure polyethylene /67/

Additive	M.p. of additive, °C	Dielectric loss factor at 10^6 sec^{-1}	Electric volume resistivity, ohm·cm·10^{-17}	Dielectric strength, kV/mm	Resistance to cracking, hours
None	0 .	0.0003	3	41	50
$Al_2O_3 \cdot SiO_2$	5	0.0018	0.001	36	780
Mannitol	0.1	0.0003	3	42	580
Adipic acid	0.1	0.0003	3	39	1,000

115

SETTING FORMULATIONS

When polyolefins compounded with peroxides are heated, they acquire a tridimensional structure, no longer melt at elevated temperatures and no longer dissolve in hydrocarbon solvents. The cross-linking process may be schematically represented as follows.

Decomposition of peroxide by heating:

$$R-O-O-R \longrightarrow 2RO\cdot$$

Formation of macroradicals:

$$RO\cdot + \cdots -CH_2-\underset{\underset{R}{|}}{\overset{\overset{H}{|}}{C}}-CH_2-\cdots \longrightarrow ROH + \cdots -CH_2-\underset{\underset{R}{|}}{\overset{\bullet}{C}}-CH_2-\cdots$$

Recombination of macroradicals:

$$2\cdots -CH_2-\overset{\bullet}{C}-CH_2-\cdots \longrightarrow \begin{matrix} \cdots -CH_2-\underset{\underset{|}{|}}{\overset{\overset{R}{|}}{C}}-CH_2-\cdots \\ \cdots -CH_2-\underset{\underset{R}{|}}{C}-CH_2-\cdots \end{matrix}$$

The considerable degree of cross-linking which is attained as a result of such processes can only be explained by assuming migration to the active center, which accelerates the recombination reactions, as has been seen above in the case of radiation-chemical cross-linking. The cross-linking of the polymer is accompanied by degradation, which is particularly high during the cross-linking of branched polyolefins: polyisobutylene, poly-propylene, ethylene-propylene copolymers.

The cross-linking agents used include benzoyl peroxide, hydroperoxides, dicumyl peroxide, tert-butyl peroxide, etc. /70, 71/. The degradation rate may be retarded by using peroxides in combination with sulfur. One of the best cross-linking compositions for polypropylene includes 4.5% dicumyl peroxide and 0.5% sulfur /72/. During the cross-linking the sulfur appears not only to suppress the degradation reactions, but also to react with the macroradicals produced by the peroxide, with formation of R−S−R type cross-links /73/. Cross-linking coagents other than sulfur include quinonedioxide, dinitrobenzene, various monomers (divinylbenzene, divinyl adipate, diallyl phthalate, etc.), polyfunctional polymers (unsaturated epoxy and polyester resins), etc. /74, 75/.

The main distinctive feature of the setting ethylene formulations is that they exhibit relatively high resistance to heat. Depending on the desired properties of the final product, it may be more expedient to increase the resistance to heat by cross-linking agents or by ionizing radiation. Thus, peroxide cross-linking may not be desirable if it is desired to retain the high dielectric parameters of the product as well as to increase its resistance to heat.

Peroxide cross-linking, just like radiation-chemical cross-linking, improves the resistance of polyethylene to cracking /76−78/.

DYEABLE FORMULATIONS

Polyolefins possess no affinity to dyestuffs and are accordingly difficult to dye. To this day, the main technique of dyeing polyolefins is to incorporate the dye or the pigment into the bulk of the polymer /7, p. 195; 17, p. 120; 79 − 82/. The attendant difficulties are connected with the migration of the dye to the surface of the article, deterioration of dielectric properties (increase of dielectric loss factor), the fastness of the dyes to heat and light and the necessity for a homogeneous distribution of the dye in the polymer.

Recently proposed dyeing techniques are based on the reaction between the dye and a deliberately introduced minor component of the formula, and are of potential interest to industry. The takeup of dyes by polypropylene may be increased by introducing small amounts of low-molecular (e. g., stearic acid) /83/ or high-molecular (e. g., polycarbonate) /84/ polar substances.

Dyeing of such polymers may be rendered more effective by incorporating metal ions forming complexes with azo dyes into the polymer /85 − 97/. Such metals include nickel, chromium, cobalt, magnesium, manganese, iron, vanadium, copper, aluminum, zinc and strontium. Salts of these metals (halides, sulfates, oxalates, phosphates, benzoates, salicylates, cyanides, acetates, stearates, thiocyanates, citrates, etc.) are added in amounts varying between 0.1 and 6%. The color imparted to the polyolefin by treatment with hot dispersions of azo dyes is fast to light and is resistant to the action of solvents, to abrasion and to heat.

Bibliography

1. British Patent 893540. 1962.
2. U. S. Patent 3153681. 1964.
3. French Patent 1350905. 1964.
4. Polochocki, A. Polimery tworzywa wielkocząsteczkowe, 10(1):23. 1965.
5. U. S. Patent 3137672. 1964.
6. Japanese Patent 7345. 1966.
7. Freund, L. and L. Ambrose. Polipropilen (Polypropylene), p.196, edited by V. I. Pilipovskii and I. K. Yartsev. − Izdatel'stvo "Khimiya." 1967.
8. Austrian Patent 224190. 1962.
9. British Patent 856793. 1961.
10. Slonimskii, G. L., I. N. Musaelyan, and V. V. Kazantseva. − Vysokomolekulyarnye Soedineniya, 6:219. 1964.
11. Newberg, R. G., D. W. Young, and H. C. Evans. − Mod. Plast., No. 12:119. 1948.
12. Rylov, E. E. and V. L. Karpov. − ZhFKh, 27:579. 1953.
13. Fel'dman, R. I. and A. K. Mironova. − Kolloidnyi Zhurnal, 19:654. 1957.
14. Delektorskii, G. P. − Vestnik Elektropromyshlennosti, No. 9:9. 1960.
15. Alekseenko, V. I. and I. U. Mishustin. − Plast. Massy, No. 2:8. 1960.

16. Martynov, M.A., V.M. Yuzhin, A.I. Malushin, and G.F. Tkachenko. — Plast. Massy. No. 10:6. 1965.
17. Shifrina, V.S. and N.N. Samosatskii. Polietilen (Polyethylene), p. 134. — Goskhimizdat. 1961.
18. Slonimskii, G.L., I.N. Musaelyan, and V.V. Kazantseva.— Vysokomolekulyarnye Soedineniya, 6:823. 1964.
19. Railsback, H.E. and R.C. Wheat. — Rubber Age, 82(4):664. 1958.
20. U.S. Patent 3123583. 1964.
21. Slonimskii, G.L., I.N. Musaelyan, V.V. Kazantseva, and G.M. Ozerov. Vysokomolekulyarnye Soedineniya, 6:818. 1964.
22. Mikhailov, N.V., E.Z. Fainberg, V.O. Gorbacheva, and C.H. Chéng.— Vysokomolekulyarnye Soedineniya, 4:237. 1962.
23. Shitov, V.V. — Elektrotekhnika, No. 12:13. 1963.
24. U.S. Patent 3231636. 1966.
25. GFR Patent 1106450. 1961.
26. British Patent 893604. 1962.
27. Austrian Patent 223813. 1962.
28. Finnish Patent 32722. 1963.
29. Fil'bert, D.V., V.P. Murav'eva, and A.B. Pakshver. — In: "Karbotsepnye volokna," p. 189, Izdatel'stvo "Khimiya." 1966.
30. U.S. Patent 3018263. 1962.
31. Japanese Patent 12786. 1961.
32. French Patent 1284591. 1962.
33. Zverev, M.P., R.A. Bychkov, and T.F. Kostin. — Khim. Volokna, No. 3:15. 1964.
34. Chem. Engng. News, 41(25):41. 1963.
35. Gul', V.E. and E.G. Lyubeshkina. — Doklady AN SSSR, 165(1):110. 1965.
36. Gul', V.E., E.G. Lyubeshkina, and A.M. Shargorodskii.— Mekhanika Polimerov, No. 6:3. 1965.
37. Gul', V.E. and E.G. Lyubeshkina. — Plast. Massy, No. 1:68. 1966.
38. Lyubeshkina, E.G., R.V. Torner, and V.E. Gul'. — Mekhanika Polimerov, No. 2:200. 1967.
39. Soviet Patent 184432. 1966.
40. Lyubeshkina, E.G., R.V. Torner, and V.E. Gul'. — Plast. Massy, No. 5:60. 1967.
41. Masakazu Inoue. — J. Polymer Sci., A1:3427. 1963.
42. Barton, J., and J. Rak. — J. Appl. Polymer Sci., 11:499. 1967.
43. Gul', V.E., E.A. Penskaya, V.N. Kuleznev, and S.G. Arutyunova. — Doklady AN SSSR, 160 (1):154. 1965.
44. Fil'bert, D.V., V.P. Murav'eva, and Yu.V. Glazkovskii.— In: "Karbotsepnye volokna," p. 82, Izdatel'stvo "Khimiya." 1966.
45. Gul', V.E., E.A. Penskaya, and V.N. Kuleznev. — Kolloidnyi Zhurnal, 27(3):341. 1965.
46. Penskaya, E.A., O.E. Dubov, and V.E. Gul'. — Doklad na simpoziume po sintezu, modifikatsii i pererabotke poliolefinov, noyabr' 1967 g. Tezisy dokladov, p. 107, Baku. 1967.

47. Mirolyubov, I. N. and M. G. Sukharev. — Plast. Massy, No. 3:62. 1963.

48. Furter, W. F. — Canad. J. Chem. Engng., 42(2):77. 1964.

49. Sinegub-Lavrenko, A. A. and M. L. Morgulis. — Plast. Massy, No. 2:3. 1966.

50. Yuzhin, V. M., I. S. Shishova, M. A. Martynov, and R. I. Belova. — Plast. Massy, No. 4:10. 1967.

51. Smirnova, A. M., L. B. Kovarskaya, T. V. Raikova, and Yu. P. Toporov. — Kolloidnyi Zhurnal, 25(6):683. 1964.

52. Ainbinder, S. B. and N. G. Andreeva. — Mekhanika Polimerov, No. 5:873. 1967; No. 6: 1070. 1967.

53. Solomko, V. P. and I. A. Uskov. — In: "Modifikatsiya svoistv polimerov i polimernykh materialov, p. 77, Kiev, Izdatel'stvo "Naukova Dumka." 1965.

54. Solomko, V. P., T. A. Molokoedova, A. A. Chuiko, and T. R. Lashko. — In: "Sintez i fiziko-khimiya polimerov," merov," p. 171, Kiev, Izdatel'stvo "Naukova Dumka." 1966.

55. Akutin, M. S., A. V. Uvarov, and G. M. Ozerov. — Doklad na simpoziume po sintezu, modifikatsii i pererabotke poliolefinov, noyabr' 1967 g. Tezisy dokladov, p. 80, Baku. 1967.

56. Chuiko, A. A. and E. A. Chuiko. — In: "Sintez i fiziko-khimiya polimerov," p. 83, Kiev, Izdatel'stvo "Naukova Dumka." 1964.

57. Solomko, V. P., T. A. Molokoedova, A. A. Chuiko, and T. R. Lashko. — In: "Sintez i fiziko-khimiya polimerov," p. 171, Kiev, Izdatel'stvo "Naukova Dumka." 1966.

58. U. S. Patent 2991264. 1961.

59. Kargin, V. A., T. I. Sogolova, and I. I. Kurbanova. — Doklady AN SSSR, 162(5):1092. 1965.

60. Sogolova, T. I. — Mekhanika Polimerov, No. 1:5. 1965.

61. Kuhre, C. J., M. Wates, and M. E. Doyle. — SPE J., 20(10):1113. 1964.

62. Kargin, V. A., T. I. Sogolova, and T. K. Shaposhnikova. — Vysokomolekulyarnye Soedineniya, 7(2):229. 1965.

63. Kargin, V. A., T. I. Sogolova, and T. K. Shaposhnikova. — Vysokomolekulyarnye Soedineniya, 7(3):385. 1965.

64. Kargin, V. A., B. P. Pashinin, V. N. Kotrelev, and M. S. Akutin. — Vysokomolekulyarnye Soedineniya, 8(12):2097. 1966.

65. Kargin, V. A., T. I. Sogolova, and I. I. Kurbanova. — Vysokomolekulyarnye Soedineniya, 8(12):2104. 1966.

66. Kargin, V. A., T. I. Sogolova, and V. M. Rubshtein. — Vysokomolekulyarnye Soedineniya, A9(2):288. 1967.

67. Nalivaiko, E. I., A. G. Sirota, P. A. Il'chenko, and I. S. Shishova. — Mekhanika Polimerov, No. 1:67. 1968.

68. Nalivaiko, E. I. and A. G. Sirota. — Plast. Massy, No. 2:13. 1968.

69. Soviet Patent 203889. 1967.

70. Amberg, L. O. Vulcanization of Elastomers (edited by G. Alliger and I. J. Sjothun). — New York, Reinhold. 1964.

71.   Seidov, N. M.   Novyi sinteticheskii kauchuk na osnove etilena i propilena (New Synthetic Rubber Based on Ethylene and Propylene), p. 53. — Baku, Azerbaidzhanskoe Gosudarstvennoe Izdatel'stvo. 1966.

72.   Manázek, Z. and D. Bellus.   Polipropilen (Polypropylene), p. 154, edited by V. I. Pilipovskii and I. K. Yartsev. — Izdatel'stvo "Khimiya." 1967.

73.   Wei, P. E. and J. Renner. — J. Polymer Chem. Technol., No. 1:35. 1962.

74.   Robinson, A. E., J. V. Marra, and L. O. Amberg. — Ind. Eng. Chem., 1(2):78. 1962.

75.   Lanas, L. P. — Ind. Eng. Chem., 2(3):202. 1963.

76.   U. S. Patent 3123583. 1964.

77.   U. S. Patent 3046238. 1962.

78.   French Patent 1337063. 1963.

79.   Kerzhkovskaya, E. M. — In: "Pererabotka plasticheskikh mass," p. 187. 1966.

80.   Destable, A. — Ind. Plast. Mod., 9(6):41. 1957.

81.   Kaufmann, K. A. — Mod. Plast., 36(6):137. 1959.

82.   Bal'tenas, R. A., R. K. Ankundinova, Ya. Yu. Bal'tenene, and I. I. Kryauchyunas. — Doklad na simpoziume po sintezu, modifikatsii i pererabotke poliolefinov, noyabr' 1967 g; Tezisy dokladov, Baku. 1967.

83.   U. S. Patent 3231530. 1966.

84.   Japanese Patent 20376. 1961.

85.   Japanese Patent 17714. 1966.

86.   Japanese Patent 17715. 1966.

87.   Japanese Patent 18911. 1966.

88.   Japanese Patent 18912. 1966.

89.   Japanese Patent 18914. 1966.

90.   Japanese Patent 20428. 1966.

91.   Japanese Patent 20430. 1966.

92.   Japanese Patent 20431. 1966.

93.   Japanese Patent 20432. 1966.

94.   Japanese Patent 20433. 1966.

95.   Japanese Patent 20434. 1966.

96.   Japanese Patent 829. 1967.

97.   Japanese Patent 830. 1967.